Herbal
Horsekeeping

Herbal
Horsekeeping

Robert McDowell and Di Rowling

J. A. Allen

This book is dedicated to Dorothy Hall my teacher, and one of those few who carried the baton during the tough times.

R. M.

This book is dedicated to all the wonderful horses who helped me acquire the knowledge to edit and craft this book (in particular Dreamie, ever the willing guinea pig!), and my partner Ron, who spurred me on to persevere with this project when everyone else had given up on ever seeing it in print.

D. R.

The authors would like to thank the following photographers for their valuable contribution to this book: Jenny Grinlington; Dolly van Zaane; Geoff Bryant; Iain Burns; Steven Foster; Kit Houghton and Matthew Roberts.

ISBN 0 85131 874 6

J.A. Allen
Clerkenwell House
Clerkenwell Green
London EC1R 0HT

J.A. Allen is an imprint of Robert Hale Limited

British Library Cataloguing in Publication Data
A catalogue record for this book is available from the British Library

Design by Judy Linard
Edited by Jane Lake
Colour separation by Tenon & Polert Colour Scanning Limited, Hong Kong
Printed by Kyodo Printing Co (S'pore) Pte Ltd, Singapore

Contents

Preface   11
Horses, Humans and Herbs   11

Introduction   13
The Traditional Healers   14
The 'Alternative' Revolution   15
The Need For Knowledge   17

PART 1 **The Herbs**   19
1 **Understanding Herbs**   21
Why Herbs?   21
How Herbs 'Work'   22
Which Herbs?   24

2 **Preparing Herbs**   26
Collecting and Drying Herbs   26
Storing Herbs   32
Dose Levels and How To Feed Herbs   39
Tips and Traps   47

3 **Growing Herbs**   51
Herbal Hedgerows   52
The Herb Garden   54
Choosing Herbs   56

PART 2 **Herbs and the Horse** 59

4 **Herbs for General Health** 61
Treating the Whole Horse 61
Nerve Tonics 65
Electrolytes 71
Allergies and Blood Cleansing 73
Worming 75
Anti-inflammatories 76
Antibiotics 79
Antioxidants 83
Poultices 84
Supplements and Common Sense 88
Herbal First Aid 91
Natural Trauma Treatment 95
Vaccinations and Injections 99

5 **Herbs and the Performance Horse** 102
Perfect Health 102
Herbal Performance Enhancement 103
Prevention of Injury 117
Rest and Recuperation 118
Herbs and Legal Competition 120
The Prepurchase Vet Check 120

6 **Herbs and Breeding** 122
The Stallion 123
The Broodmare 125
The Youngster 126

7 **Herbs and Traveling** 130
Worst-case Traveling Scenarios 131
Training 131
Trailer/Truck Design 132
Private Transportation 133
Commercial Transportation 134
Herbal Travel Treatments 135

8 **Sharing Herbs with your Horse** 139

9 **Herbs and the Other Therapies** 142
Homeopathy and Bach Flowers 142

Other Alternative Therapies 150
Herbs and Veterinary Science 152

10 **Specific Conditions** 153
Allergic Reactions 154
Anemia 155
Azoturia (Tying up) 158
Bones and Connective Tissues 160
Cuts, Abrasions and Wounds 167
Digestive System 168
Eye Conditions 175
Hoof Conditions 178
Respiratory System 187
Skin Conditions 200
Stringhalt 208
Tetanus 209
Recovery, Recuperation and Radiance 210

11 **Basic Recipes** 217
Rosehip Tea 217
Chamomile Tea 217
Tendon, Ligament, Scar-tissue Poultice 218
Drawing Poultice 218
Antiseptic/Styptic 218
Tendon and Bone Mix 218
Internal Ulcer and Scours Mix 219
Show-coat Mix 219
Hoof Oil 219
Anemia Mix 220
Chest and Immunity Mix 220
Allergic Rhinitis Mix 221

12 **Case Studies** 223
Buck 223
Kachét 225
Bracket Jack 226
Pepper 227
Jackson 228
Shalimar 229
Carmelita 230
Harry 231

PART 3 Materia Medica of Herbs — 233
The Actions of Herbs — 235

Alteratives — 235
Anodynes — 236
Antipruritics — 237
Antiseptics — 237
Antispasmodics — 238
Astringents — 238
Bitters — 239
Carminatives — 239
Cathartics — 240
Demulcents and Emollients — 240
Diuretics and Diaphoretics — 240
Emmenogogues — 242
Febrifuges — 242
Hepatics — 242
Laxatives — 243
Nervines — 243
Rubefacients — 244
Vermicides and Vermifuges — 245
Vulnaries — 245

The List of Herbs — 246

Alfalfa/Lucerne (*Medicago sativa*) — 246
Aloes (*Aloe vera*) — 247
Arnica (*Arnica montana*) — 248
Borage (*Borago officinalis*) — 248
Buckwheat (*Fagopyrum esculentum*) — 249
Calendula/Marigold (*Calendula officinalis*) — 249
Castor Oil (*Ricinus communis*) — 250
Celery (*Apium graveolens*) — 250
Chamomile (*Anthemis nobilis*) — 251
Chickweed (*Stellaria media*) — 252
Comfrey/Knitbone (*Symphytum officinale*) — 252
Dandelion/Wet-The-Bed (*Taraxacum officinale*) — 253
Devil's Claw (*Harpogophytum procumbens*) — 254
Echinacea (*Echinacea purpurea*) — 254
Equisetum/Horsetail (*Equisetum arvense*) — 255
Elecampane (*Inula helenium*) — 255
Eucalyptus (*Eucalyptus globulus*) — 256
Fennel (*Foeniculum vulgare*) — 257

Fenugreek (*Trigonella foenum-graecum*)   257
Garlic (*Allium sativum*)   258
Golden Seal (*Hydrastis canadensis*)   259
Hawthorn (*Crataegus oxycanthus*)   259
Hops (*Humulus lupulus*)   261
Horehound (*Marrubrium vulgare*)   262
Horseradish (*Cochlearia armoracia*)   262
Hypericum/St Johns Wort (*Hypericum perforatum*) 263
Juniper (*Juniperus communis*)   264
Kelp/ bladderwrack (*Fucus vesiculosus*)   264
Linseed/Flax Seed (*Linum usitatissimum*)   265
Male Fern (*Dryopteris filix-mas*)   266
Maritime Pine (*Pinus pinaster*)   266
Mullein (*Verbascum thapsus*)   267
Nettle/Stinging Nettle (*Urtica dioica*)   267
Oats (*Avena sativa*)   268
Parsley (*Petroselinum crispum*)   269
Passion Flower (*Passiflora incarnata*)   269
Pennyroyal (*Mentha pulegiuim*)   270
Peppermint (*Mentha piperita*)   270
Raspberry Leaf (*Rubus idaeus*)   271
Red Clover (*Trifolium pratense*)   271
Rosehips/Briar Rose (*Rosa canina*)   272
Rosemary (*Rosmarinus officinalis*)   272
Rue (*Ruta graveolens*)   273
Sage (*Salvia officinalis*)   274
Slippery Elm (*Ulmus fulva*)   275
Tansy (*Tanacetum vulgare*)   275
Thuja (*Thuja occidentalis*)   276
Thyme (*Thymus vulgaris*)   276
Valerian (*Valeriana officinalis*)   277
Vervain (*Verbena officinalis*)   278
White Willow (*Salix alba*)   278
Wintergreen (*Gaultheria procumbens*)   279
Wormwood (*Artemisia absinthium*)   279
Yarrow/Woundwort (*Achillea millefolium*)   280

References   281

Index   283

Disclaimer

The authors and publisher cannot be held responsible for the adverse reaction of any horse to a particular herb (or combination of herbs), homeopathic remedy, recommended feedstuff, additive, or training/handling suggestion. In serious, or potentially serious, situations professional advice should always be sought.

A Note on Measurements

The measurements used in the book are metric in the main. Where we have used 'cups' , 'tablespoons' and 'teaspoons' etc. this refers to the standard measurements:

    1 cup = 250 ml

    1 tablespoon = 20 ml

    1 teaspoon = 5 ml

    1 kilogram = 2.2 lb

A feed 'scoop' is roughly the equivalent of 3 liters (3 quarts). A 'handful' is quite simply that!

Preface

Horses, Humans and Herbs

My first involvement with equine herbal medicine came many years ago following a meeting with an Irish veterinary herbalist in the Lisdoo Arms, a small country pub in Ireland. This man's name is Tom O'Hanlon and I still have the pages and pages of notes I made during that session. Tom's knowledge came from his mother who was from a French Gypsy background, and he had extensive knowledge of harvesting and mixing up herbs for treating horses and farm animals.

On finding out that I was a practicing medical herbalist – for humans – Tom was interested in exchanging information, because farmers constantly asked him for advice about their own ailments. As we spoke, it became apparent that most of the herbs he was using for animals, I was using for humans to treat similar conditions, and so I could reassure him that, in most cases, there is no harm in treating a human as he would an animal. Then we spent our time discussing all the herbs we used commonly and comparing their efficacy in both animal and human treatment.

This occupied a cold winter's afternoon – and I must admit to being very glad I took the notes because I find my memory stops working after three pints of Guinness, although Tom was perfectly lucid after twice that many! Tom departed for a round of his clients in England (these days he is frantically busy in England, Ireland and France); synchronicity 'clicked in', and on my return to Australia my human patients started asking me about treatments for their animals! The result has been a very busy herbal practice treating human, equine and canine patients.

My co-author, Di Rowling, and I have published many magazine articles on herbs and horses over the years: Di's writing/editing skills and horse knowledge complementing my herbal knowledge and experience. This book evolved as a direct response to requests from horse owners all over the world who read those articles, and from my numerous horse-owning patients, for us to provide a comprehensive yet accessible text that will give horse owners the knowledge to maintain and treat their horses as nature intended.

Robert McDowell, March 2003

Introduction

Before we kept horses in artificial environments, they roamed free across large tracts of land, and kept themselves healthy by grazing on a large variety of grasses, grains, herbs and other seasonal plants. Horses not only grazed like this, but also sought out mineral-salt deposits – in fact, all the deposits mined commercially have been discovered by animals that used them as salt licks. Horses roaming near coastal areas also regularly used seaweed as a source of minerals and trace elements. Because they had freedom of choice, they followed their instincts to eat the plants and seek out the minerals they needed for certain times of the year (breeding, coming up to hard winters, etc.), and 'self-medicated' for any deficiencies, or existing or impending health or injury problems.

Just as the lifestyle of modern man is very different from the lifestyle of our forbears, the lives our horses live are very different from that of the horse in his natural state. We confine our equines to small pastures with limited (and sometimes no) grazing; we limit their exercise to short periods of planned, structured workouts tailored for the specific sports; we feed processed foodstuffs with chemical additives; and we medicate with pharmaceutical chemicals. It is little wonder that the health of the modern horse is fragile and that owners are seeking a return to more traditional health-care methods for themselves and their equine charges. One of the oldest and most effective health-care arts is that of the herbalist, and herbs are proving to be a simple and efficacious means of maintaining optimum equine health for a growing number of horse owners.

Most horse owners have experienced their horses pulling towards different weeds along the side of the road, or eating their feces, turning up their noses at something offered to them, or even sampling all sorts of 'odd' things if they happen to get into the vegetable garden. Basically, horses already know what they need for optimum health – we just have to learn how to give it to them – and that can be the tricky part given our twenty-first century consciousness (or perhaps lack of it)! The first step in understanding how to return our horsekeeping to a more natural state is to understand the origins of herbal knowledge which, interestingly, owes much to the instincts of animals.

The Traditional Healers

People in ancient times had more time on their hands for observation and lived in close association with nature, which resulted in a good practical knowledge of herbal remedies. Nature helped by 'color coding' plants, with poisonous berries often being black, or foul smelling, or bad tasting, while others attract by their appearance or their taste. There have been those of each generation who took a special interest in healing, who listened, collected, accumulated, experimented and practiced with this knowledge. They became the 'practitioners' of that generation, but every mother and farmer knew all the basics of herbal and natural medicine, which they needed for their day-to-day health. This 'common sense' has been lost to latter day generations.

Much of the knowledge of herbal lore was also acquired in early times by animal herders, who had no fences to contain their charges and who spent their lives watching and worrying about their animals. The herders spent a large part of their lives watching their animals feeding and they noticed the animals seeking out herbs and weeds in their pasture at different times. They also, of course, connected this with the idea that the choice of particular herbs related to health, injury, and seasonal or reproductive demands of the animals. The animals already 'knew' what they needed; it was built into their instincts.

These days – because we have given over the responsibility of our health and that of our animals to doctors, vets, conventional medical ideas and drugs – we have mostly forgotten this ancient knowledge. Learning about herbs, and which herbs are beneficial for ourselves and our horses, is really a relearning and is all about developing the technique of 'listening' to the instinctive knowledge horses have about maintaining their own health. Using herbs effectively is also very much about developing intuition and confidence in our own abilities, as well as acquiring a working understanding of herbs and their actions.

The 'Alternative' Revolution

The term 'alternative therapy' has been used to differentiate between treatment with natural therapies and treatment by doctors of medicine, and yet the practice of treatment with herbal medicine is as old as time itself. In reality it is the traditional medicine. A less controversial term which is gaining in popularity is 'complementary medicine'. However, for consistency with modern terminology, we will refer to the traditional therapies as 'alternative'.

The past twenty-five years have seen alternative medicine in human health care change from a practice only used by a fringe minority to one of mainstream acceptance. This revolution is still gaining momentum, with orthodox medicine now scrambling to claim herbs for their own purposes to treat drug resistant viral and bacterial infections, as well as AIDS, cancers and an ever-increasing array of illnesses that really seem to be a result of the twentieth century more than anything else.

In the horse industry, there has always been an acceptance of the old-fashioned remedies passed down through the generations, but these have been mostly shouldered aside in the past forty years by a spectacular growth in the veterinary, feed and supplement industries. Interestingly, during the same forty-year period, in relative terms, horses have become more fragile, more highly strung and more expensive to maintain than at any previous time in history.

It is no coincidence that big business now permeates the whole of the equine industry, as it is a huge industry in monetary terms all over the world. Big business is involved in every aspect of horses and their care, from breeding, rearing, feed supplements, vitamins and feed additives, veterinary care and medicines, to competition, gambling (legal and otherwise), taxation income and illegal performance-enhancing drugs.

Australia, the home country of the authors, is one of the world leaders in the manufacture and supply of high-quality veterinary growth hormones widely used in the equine industry and commonly abused by human athletes and body builders worldwide.

The horse's health and wellbeing certainly have not benefited from this situation. One is led to wonder what happened to the talented horse that was largely pasture fed and to a large degree looked after his own health. In times of need these owners would consult with the farrier or neighbor or a do-it-yourself health book for advice on treatment of illness and injury, not turn to immediate surgery or pharmaceutical drugs as a first step.

Horse care is following directly in the path of the movement in human health care toward alternative therapies for exactly the same reasons: owners seek an alternative to drugs and invasive veterinary practices to treat the ever-increasing number of equine health problems. All this sounds unbelievable in an environment where science and the supplement and drug industries seem dominant and claim to have the answers to all of our questions. The fact is, however, that scientific medicine (human and veterinary) is in crisis. Antibiotics, having been over-prescribed for forty years, no longer work as they used to. Our medical institutions are now infested by super-resistant bacteria and are dangerous places to go to. Viral infections are crossing species lines, cancers and immune-system diseases are proliferating much faster than we can control them, and the whole western medical infrastructure is so expensive worldwide that it threatens to send entire economies bankrupt.

In the equine industry all this is also true and owners and trainers are poised to completely change the way they feed and medicate their horses. Vets are suddenly embracing alternative modalities like acupuncture, massage and chiropractic – even herbalism.

The word 'herbal' is appearing on products on stock-feed shelves as the multinational manufacturers seek to dominate and claim for themselves the flow of information into this market. This comes at a time when a large number of people worldwide have already experienced the effectiveness of herbal medicine on their own health ailments, and they now desire to apply it to their horse's health. In marketing terms, this is a 'bonanza' opportunity!

The Need For Knowledge

As a result of the 'alternative revolution', there are an increasing number of alternative practitioners entering the horse industry across the world. Like any profession, however, there are good and bad practitioners in the herbal and alternative therapies; some herbalists are unethical or just plain 'no good' in the same way as some vets and doctors are unethical or just plain 'no good'.

This means that now, more than ever, horse owners need to become knowledgeable about alternative modalities, including herbs, so they can make their own informed decisions about their own animal's health and can, therefore, better judge their various practitioners. Acquiring this knowledge has the added bonus of equipping the horse owner with invaluable tools in feeding, caring for and medicating horses using highly effective, safe, cheap and natural substances.

This book aims to explain the way in which herbs can form the basis of a health regimen to keep our equine partners in top form without the need for chemicals and unnecessary invasive veterinary practices. The information in the following pages is certainly not designed to provide the reader with all the knowledge to completely replace the need for veterinary care – rather it is designed to provide natural alternatives to chemical horsekeeping. The province of the herbalist will always be in preventing the onset of disease in the first place; in supporting metabolic systems in recovery from illness; and in dealing with long-term or chronic conditions that defy modern veterinary treatments. Certainly it is advisable to avoid where possible the use of chemical preparations in caring for your horse but, in times of trauma or acute illness, the following is a sensible course of action. First, use alternative therapies and common sense first-aid techniques to stem blood flow and to treat shock, then immediately engage an experienced veterinary practitioner to use all the modern life-saving tools at his or her disposal. Go on to support the veterinary treatment with the judicious use of herbal preparations and professional advice during recovery.

In terms of day-to-day horsekeeping and non-acute or life-threatening conditions, the information in this book will give you a rudimentary understanding of using herbs yourself to treat your horse. You will also be provided with enough knowledge to ascertain when to seek the advice of a professional herbalist, as well as gain a sufficient understanding to determine the level of expertise of that practitioner.

The book is divided into three sections – Part One deals with herbs and the horse; Part Two looks specifically at the main herbs used in treating horses, and Part Three is the materia medica.

In Part One, we will look first at the way in which herbs work to maintain a horse's health, and to correct imbalances by treating the 'whole horse' as opposed to treating symptoms. It will also look at how to choose herbs, the various ways to prepare the herbs, and how to grow your own herbs.

Then in Part Two, we will concentrate on the use of herbs in broad health and wellbeing areas. We will look at herbs for performance horses and for breeding; offer suggestions for sharing herbs with your horse; and give brief explanations of how the herbalist's art fits in with other alternative modalities and conventional veterinary medicine. There is also a comprehensive section on using herbs to treat and to support conventional treatments for specific common equine ailments and conditions.

The final section of Part Two provides several 'real life' case studies encountered in equine herbal practice, which illustrate common patterns of treatment and recovery.

Part Three is an alphabetical materia medica of the main herbs for horses, with pictures of these to help you identify them in your surroundings.

PART 1
The Herbs

1 Understanding Herbs

Why Herbs?

As with people, the modern horse's natural immunity has been savagely depleted by abuse in the last few decades. As mentioned earlier, a horse has highly refined instincts that allow him to self-medicate by seeking out and grazing on a huge variety of plants, weeds and herbs. Instead of working with these instincts, modern horsekeeping practices see our horses locked away on 'improved' pasture. We replace hedgerows with fences and feed concentrated and chemically prepared or treated feed. We then go on to subvert the natural exercise patterns they would use to recover from work injury or stress by locking them up in stables, and then insisting upon brief, short and highly structured bursts of exercise.

By taking horses away from their natural environment, we have created for ourselves the task of feeding them a balanced diet, because most of us do not own huge tracts of land on which to turn our horses free. Most people today, in the quest to provide the 'best' nutrition, spend copious amounts of money a year on commercially produced supplements that lay claim to everything from enhancing performance, through making a heavy coat fall out, to calming a horse's temperament. Not only do most of these products simply just not work, many of them are positively deleterious to the wellbeing of the horse.

Our horsekeeping practices are not creating a generation of robust and healthy horses; they have, in fact, made the immune systems of our current generation of horses the most fragile in the history of horsekeeping. Not only has our care regimen become extremely expensive, but it has also become extremely complex. The answer to restoring health and wellbeing is to simplify, and to seek the ancient knowledge that has kept thousands of generations of horses healthy through the centuries. Simple common remedies like garlic, lemon, dandelion, nettle, rosehips, kelp, fenugreek, and comfrey, to name a few, are deceptively powerful and will form the basis of 'bullet-proof' health for your horse.

The vitamins, minerals, trace elements and proteins contained in herbs have the major advantage of being naturally occurring food substances, and they are easily digested and absorbed when combined with standard feed products. They contain no artificial or chemical medicines or additives that could have harmful side effects or disqualify a competition horse subject to testing. In contrast to chemical medicines, they all act as metabolic tonics of various sorts, enhancing the animal's own healing abilities and maximizing performance. All you need to acquire is a basic understanding of herbs and their health-giving properties to give your horse the best shot at a long and robust life.

How Herbs 'Work'

Using herbs effectively requires that you understand how they 'work' and this requires that you relinquish the 'medical mindset'. Herbs are chosen for a particular health problem using a whole gamut of criteria, which seem at first glance to be very unscientific, haphazard and non-rigorous. Welcome to the 'art of healing' as opposed to the 'science of treating'!

When you first start experimenting and giving herbs to your horse, it is likely you will be assuming that specific herbs treat specific symptoms or illnesses; you will attempt to treat your horse on that basis. You will hear that herbs like garlic or echinacea are good for treating infection; celery for fluid retention; valerian or hypericum to calm the nerves; and wormwood for worms, etc. This is the 'medical' approach – to name a condition and then to prescribe the herb that applies to that condition.

However, traditional herbal knowledge is not listed under named conditions, except in the older herbals, which might prescribe obtuse things like 'celery for dropsy' or 'buchu for scrofulous'. This information is simply confusing, but if you continue to peruse the old herbals, you will begin to understand their systems of diagnosis, and to get the feeling that herbs are mostly described in terms of body processes, not named diseases. This is the first important lesson.

For example, the action of the herb vervain might be described as 'antispasmodic, nervine, tonic, sedative and hepatic'; the action of white willow described as 'analgesic, anti-inflammatory, tonic, astringent, antiseptic and febrifuge'. This is more helpful, since there are only a certain number of these old-fashioned words used to describe actions, and when you become familiar with them, you can begin to develop a picture in your head of each herb in terms of its range of action.

Nowadays, we all know what antispasmodic means, as well as antiseptic, sedative, tonic and anti-inflammatory. Hepatic means 'for the liver' and febrifuge means 'to reduce fever'. This might begin to look tricky – but relax!

For the purposes of using herbs today, the actions of each herb do not have to be memorized as they were in medical schools in the Middle Ages. We have included a materia medica at the back of the book for easy reference, along with a listing and description of the terms used to describe their actions – but read it later. Just allow your understanding of each herb to develop in your mind along the lines of the body systems to which they seem to apply, and their individual range of actions.

For example, the actions of white willow are fairly straightforward, and it is necessary to separate in your understanding the analgesic, anti-inflammatory and febrifuge from the tonic, astringent and antiseptic properties of the herb. No herbalist uses white willow as their primary antiseptic because there are dozens of other better antiseptic herbs, however it is interesting to note that white willow is also classed as a tonic and as an astringent. All the actions of white willow considered together support the notion that this herb would be effective in treating pain, fever, wounds and swelling. This is what we use it for.

Similarly, even though one of the actions of the herb vervain is listed as hepatic, no professional herbalist would ever prescribe vervain for liver complaints, simply because there are many much more common and more effective hepatic herbs than vervain – two examples being the common dandelion and St Mary's thistle. Vervain is infinitely more valuable in treating nervous-system disorders.

This sort of general knowledge is really all you need to acquire in order to treat your horse with the basic herbal remedies. The requirements are a good understanding of the main herbs useful for treating horses; an understanding of the way herbs 'work' on the body systems; and a willingness to develop a 'feel' and an intuition for finding the right herb for the job. This will come with practice. Then simply add to this a generous dose of common or 'horse' sense and employ it regularly.

Which Herbs?

When confronted by a health problem with your horse, or searching for a maintenance feeding regimen to forestall health problems, it is necessary to have a repertoire of available herbs from which to choose. These come from various sources. Simply because an herb comes from far away, is expensive, difficult to obtain, or has an exotic name does not mean it is better for your purposes; often the opposite is the case.

Let us look at the herbs you will need to fulfill most of your equine needs, and where to find them – starting in your own backyard.

Common and Local Weeds, Herbs and Grains

These common plants are always the first to get to know and to choose from. Get to know the herbs growing in your local area. In temperate areas of the Western world you will find most of the following valuable herbs growing:

alfalfa (lucerne), aloe vera, bladderack (kelp), borage, broom, buckwheat, castor oil plant, celery, comfrey, couch grass, corn silk, dandelion, fennel, garlic, hawthorn, horehound, horseradish, horse chestnut, hypericum (St Johns wort), lavender, linseed, millet, mistletoe, nettle, oats, parsley, peppermint, red clover, raspberry, rosehips, rosemary, rue, sage, St Mary's thistle, shepherds purse, thyme, wild lettuce, wormwood, yarrow.

Culinary and Other Commercial Herbs

This group of herbs is the next to consider, and they are readily available from health-food stores and supermarkets:

cayenne pepper, chamomile, fenugreek, ginger, senna.

Popular Herbs and Treatments from the Health Food Store

These herbs are all common and are becoming more and more widely available, either dried or in various preparations like ointments or extracts:

arnica, calendula, devils claw, echinacea, equisetum (horsetail), ginkgo biloba, ginseng, juniper, marshmallow, passion flower, rue, sarsaparilla, skullcap, slippery elm, thuja, valerian, vervain, wild yam, witch hazel.

These three groupings contain 75% of the herbs used by many professional herbalists. This may seem surprising, but it is the truth. Herbal medicine is really all about simple applied common sense.

Anyone promoting exclusive, exotic and expensive treatments, or describing all the above herbs using their Latin (botanical) names in ordinary conversation is simply trying to keep the knowledge from you and to promote themselves as elite in some way.

The formal listing of herbs at the end of this book (the materia medica) is chosen from among the herbs above with just a few exceptions drawn from my own pharmacy, which are very specific in their action and worth going to the extra trouble to obtain.

2 Preparing Herbs

Collecting and Drying Herbs

Most herbs used in Western herbal medicine evolved in the Old World or were brought in from similar climatic regions elsewhere. Exotics from tropical regions had to be grown elsewhere, and herbalists had to rely on the experience (second-hand usually) of the natives of the countries of origin, often as reported by the sailors or the priests, or whoever 'discovered' them.

The herbs listed in the materia medica and described in this book are primarily those with a long tradition of use in the Western world. All of these are either local or have been imported along with the knowledge of their values by successive waves of migration of all sorts over the centuries.

Detailed knowledge of the exact time and manner of collection of herbs to maximize the medicinal value occupied a great deal of attention in early texts, most of which was described in an astrological context that we are no longer clever enough to understand. Astrology, of course, was the clock of all prehistoric cultures, so its use is actually not all that surprising. It is also possible that the scientists, practitioners, and philosophers of early times were very much like those of today, and – as a way of enhancing their own prestige, wealth and power – did not want to make it too easy for the masses to understand. Undoubtedly much of the complexity and ritual of harvesting has more to do with this than anything else; much like the mystique, regulation, cost structure and ritual in a modern pharmaceutical factory!

Even today, in some central European countries where herbs are still 'wild crafted' (harvested from the wild), the ladies from the village will be sent off at a certain time of the year and phase of the moon. They will be instructed to 'collect on that particular day, only from the south facing slopes and cease collection when the last of the dew has dried on the herb'. Herbs gathered in such a manner are much sought after, and there is undeniably much to be learned from the olden days on this aspect of the herbal art. However, for our purposes here it is more than adequate to simply apply 'horse sense' to the harvesting and preparation of our herbs.

All growing things have a seasonal cycle, and in plants it is more obvious than in most other living things. This is what we use these days to determine the best time to harvest.

Harvesting and Drying

As drying is the traditional way of storing herbs, it is advisable to harvest them when the maximum value is concentrated in the part of the herb you want to use.

- As a rule the 'aerial parts' (where the whole of the plant appearing above the ground is to be used) of an herb are harvested in spring or early summer when the plant has reached full maturity. The plant is cut off close to the ground, the lower stems are secured with string, and it is hung upside down in a cool dry place – just as with dried flowers or sprays of lavender.

Harvesting peppermint

Harvesting calendula   Harvesting German chamomile at Jurlique, South Australia

- When you are using the 'tops' or the fresh green growth and flowers - as with broom (*Cytisus scoparius*), hawthorn (*Crataegus oxycanthus*) or St Johns wort (*hypericum perforatum*) – harvest when the flowers are in full bloom and all the goodness is concentrated at this end of the plant. If you are just using the flowers, they are picked and dried when in full bloom.

Harvesting violets

Dried calendula flowers

Harvesting dandelions for seed

- Seeds are obviously harvested when they are ripe, often from the whole herb, which has been hung upside down over a cloth or thrashed to drop the seeds. Store the seeds in a cool, dry place.

Storing dried herbs and seeds in jars

Dried dandelion root

- Fruit or berries should be picked and stored when fully grown and ripe.
- Roots are best harvested in early winter when the plant concentrates its reserves below ground and the tops die off.

Drying is best done by hanging the plants upside down in a shaded, dry environment (like the back of a cave). Seeds and bulbs are

Above: Hanging garlic

Left: Green, fresh herbs drying

programmed to keep (like the garlic plaited and hanging in the windows of shops), so they just need to be kept dry. Most roots have to be chopped and dried in late autumn, and kept very dry.

Commercial drying racks

Fresh Herbs

Nature tells us when to harvest herbs to feed fresh to horses, which is usually when your horse is programmed to need them. In a temperate climate your horse will tell you the best time to harvest your herbs by seeking out the 'goodies' in your hedgerow. Obviously, the season for feeding fresh herb is the same as for harvesting, in the case of tops and whole herb, and later on in the case of seeds.

As a general rule of thumb, collect and feed fresh whenever your herbs are in season, because this is the best medicine for this particular time of the year. Fresh tops imported from some other part of the world and fed to your horse in the middle of winter would be very confusing and of little value to your horse's health or metabolism – rather like a person eating an artificially ripened banana in the middle of a northern winter season.

Horse eating fresh herbs

Storing Herbs

Despite the advances of modern science, the most effective methods of preserving and storing herbs for future use are those provided by history. The repositories of herbal and medical knowledge, besides the Gypsies

Monastery garden, UK

and the village herbalists of the Middle Ages, were the monks. All monasteries had herb gardens that were really medical gardens, and many of the monks specialized in treating ailments and recorded the knowledge in their writings. Monks prepared dried herbs as well as oil-and-honey-based medicines and liqueurs and it is from many of their writings that herb storage methods have been handed down to the current generation for whom they are as valid as ever.

The different methods available will depend on the kinds of herbs you have harvested, your circumstances and your intended use. So, after harvesting it is necessary to decide which will be the ideal way to store your herbs for the coming season. Nature has given us the clues for this.

Dried Plant Material

This is stored in nature as dry plant matter in the pasture or hedgerows, and horses evolved to be able to live most of the year on this sort of feed while taking seasonal advantage of fresh green pasture. Bales of alfalfa (lucerne) hay in a shed or grain in a sack in the feed shed are perfect examples of how to store dried herbs; keep them dry, keep the air circulating and the rats out as far as possible, and that is it. Some dried herbs will keep for more than one season, depending on careful

Hay bales stored to keep them dry

management of moisture and temperature variation. Your nose and eyes
will tell you how much value is left in the dried herb.

Honey, Molasses and Oil Extracts

Honey, molasses and oils store almost indefinitely. They also have several
other properties, which make them ideal mediums for the extraction and
storage of herbs.

These substances will absorb all oil-based
ingredients from fresh herbs into themselves and
preserve them indefinitely. There are many such oils,
some of which are more readily available and
cheaper to produce than others. Olive oil is a very
common 'essential oil', which is to say that it is
pressed directly out of the fruit and contains
nothing else. However, the 'essential oil' from rose
petals, for example, would require hundreds of
pounds of fresh rose petals to make very small
amounts of oil; some very expensive perfumes are
made of blends of such oils, but rose oil is not a
feasible 'carrier' for preserving herbs.

Common herbal oils, like lavender or hypericum,
are made by soaking the fresh tops and flowers of
these plants in carrier oil (usually olive oil), and
letting the oils within the herb be absorbed into the

Yarrow and calendula flowers soaking in oil

carrier. For example, hypericum (St Johns wort, which grows wild and is so prolific it is a declared noxious weed in parts of Australia), flowers over an eight to ten week period in late spring and summer. To extract the red hypericum oil from the leaves and flowers, you simply pick the tops at the first flowering and pack them into a bucket containing a good quality olive oil. After approximately three weeks you take out and drain the depleted material, and pack the same oil with a fresh batch of tops and flowers. This is repeated once more, after which you have port-wine-colored oil that contains the entire medicinal value of the St Johns wort, and will store indefinitely.

Pushing whole cloves of garlic into a bucket of molasses makes a wonderful garlic extract. Do not peel the cloves, just roll the garlic corm under your boot and pack the individual cloves in the bucket. After three weeks, all the garlic oil is in the molasses and only the husks of the corms remain. These do not even need to be removed; they can be fed along

Garlic and wormwood extract in molasses

Horse taking garlic clove

with the extract. All horses should, and can, be trained to eat fresh garlic from the hand so that at times of need (like when fighting an infection) you can give them extra doses. A fail-safe way of training a particular horse to take garlic is by feeding some molasses from a new batch to the horse each day for the three weeks it takes for the extraction to be complete. In this way all horses become accustomed to the taste and they will then take fresh garlic, which should be fed as a treat a couple of times a week; just two or three cloves each time as a preventative

Above: Garlic in honey

Left: Horse taking molasses from hand

health tonic. At times of demand, medicinal doses of up to a half dozen cloves twice a day are then easy to administer.

Honey works the same as molasses, and you can make a honey-based garlic medicine for your horse (or family) in exactly the same way.

Alcohol-based Extracts

Alcohol preserves almost indefinitely (herbs, not people!). Alcohol and water mixtures have been used in exactly the same way as oils to extract and preserve the ingredients from herbs for most of recorded history.

Many of the early wines and all the early liqueurs were herbal medicines in which dried herbs were extracted.

Again, this was a simple process. The dried tops, seed, flower, root or whole herb was chopped and packed into the wine or spirit, stirred around over a period of time (usually less than four or five weeks), and then pressed out in the wine press or olive oil press. These days, you can do the exact same thing with plastic buckets

Alcohol-based extracts in bottles

and a wine press; the commercial producers in their factories do the same with their vats, stirring drums, hydraulic presses, and filters.

It is really useful to make extracts from fresh herbs as well, and when a gardener friend found a bush of broom in flower, we picked about 1.4 kg of tops, and packed them into a 50:50 mixture of pure alcohol and rainwater for extraction. This extract was on our shelves in three weeks to treat 'gray-green' complexioned lady patients with under-functioning spleens.

Similarly, we harvest a few maritime pine trees (*Pinus pinaster*) from a nearby pine plantation for their bark and sapwood. This is put through a garden 'mulcher' and into alcohol and water mixes to produce the super antioxidant pine bark extract mentioned in the following chapters.

In human herbal practices in Australia a good many of the treatments are based on liquid-alcohol-based extracts and tinctures, unlike the Chinese and English herbalists, who mostly use dried herbs in water-based extracts (teas, infusions and decoctions), and the American herbalists, who are mostly denied access to alcohol extracts and forced to rely on dried herbs in pill form.

In the canine practice we prepare treatments mostly with alcohol-based extracts, the same as for human patients, on the assumption that both being carnivores, dogs and humans can cope equally well with the alcohol. Over fourteen years of successfully treating vast numbers of racing greyhounds for illness and performance enhancement, this assumption is now well proven.

However, in equine practice we use very few alcohol-based extracts because, as a rule, alcohol is not good for grazing animals and their livers do not cope at all well with it. Besides dried herb treatments for horses, we prepare mainly organic cider vinegar extracts from both single herbs and various mixtures of dried herbs.

Vinegar-based Extracts

Undoubtedly the idea of using vinegar to extract herbs has been around forever – as vinegar is another of those natural preservatives that is also made using fermentation in the same way as alcohol – but it does not seem to have been used extensively as an extraction medium. (Maybe everyone just liked the alcoholic medicines better!)

Using organic cider vinegar is simple, natural and chemical free. Vinegar on its own contains valuable organic acids and has astringent properties, and is palatable to horses that probably first got the taste for it by eating fermenting windfall apples in the wild.

Vinegar extracts are recommended for horses for all the following reasons:

1. In many cases an herb that is bitter or otherwise unpalatable to horses is easy to administer as a vinegar extract.

   Very small amounts of powerful or unpalatable herbs can be mixed evenly through a dried herb mix within the vinegar medium when required.

2. Herbs only commercially available as powders (many roots, woods and bark products are like this) are difficult to administer dry, but easily extract into vinegar.

   Mixtures for respiratory-system and digestive-system problems all derive direct support from the vinegar itself.

   Complex formulations of six or more herbs – including some roots, some powders, some seeds and some dried herbs – are often much more conveniently prepared in vinegar than in the dried form.

   A liquid medium allows you to mix homeopathic ingredients – like the Bach Flower Remedies – directly through a whole mix.

   Vinegar-based ingredients may be shipped and stored separately from dried herb mixes and combined at the time of application, thus improving the shelf-life of the formulation, which starts ticking away as soon as moist ingredients are added to the herbs.

3. Liquid medicines may be given against the horse's will via a drench.

4. Finally, in large stables, it is often just too difficult from a management point of view to wait and watch patiently to see that each individual horse has taken his medicine when it is presented in the dried form. While it is ideal to tap into, re-establish and use, the horse's instincts by using dried herbs, in some cases it is either 'fast herbal medicine' or 'chemical medicine', and fast herbal is certainly the preferred option.

Making the Extract

Most professional herbalists will be able to supply herbal extracts for your use but you may like to try making them yourselves.

To make a vinegar-based extract, steep (soak) the dried herb in organic cider vinegar at the rate of approximately 2 kg of herb to 10 liters of vinegar. Stir the mix occasionally, and strain out the liquid after five weeks. Press the herb sediment to get as much of the liquid out as possible. If you can find an old wine press, or one of those

Scales and cider vinegar

Dried herbs soaking in vinegar

Cider vinegar extract being squeezed through muslin

contraptions for straining and pressing home-made sauce, that will help you to get the most out of the mix but if that is not possible, then strain the mixture through muslin or a clean tea towel, and then wring out the sediment.

Working out the concentrations of the different herbs can get a little tricky, however, as different herbs will produce stronger extracts. If you want to get serious about producing your own extracts and want a stronger extract, just add enough vinegar to wet the herb when mixed. Keep adding a little vinegar as the herb swells and the top of the mix dries out. You will need to record the weight of herb and the volume of extract squeezed out. The strength of the resultant extract (given a very powerful press) is the ratio between the weight of herbs in kilograms and the volume of extract in liters.

For example, if 2 kg of herb produces 6 liters of extract after having added 10 liters of vinegar and using a hydraulic press to extract, this produces a 2:6 or (simplified) a 1:3 strength extract.

Dose Levels and How to Feed Herbs

Herb dose levels is one of the subjects that attracts a great deal of criticism from the orthodox veterinary establishment that has been brought up on dose-specific pharmaceutical products and recommended daily intake specifications from the 'science' of nutrition. In this area, we need also to dispense with the 'medical mindset' mentioned earlier.

While it is undeniably necessary to show extreme caution with pharmaceutical drugs, herbs are a different matter altogether. Care should be taken with the use and dosage of some herbs but the herbs in the doses mentioned in this book very, very rarely have side effects and very large quantities would have to be administered, almost force-fed against the horse's will, to cause any signs of upset whatsoever. The herbs in the doses given in following sections are safe for use, subject to the cautions noted in the materia medica, even for young horses, breeding stallions and pregnant or lactating mares.

Caution needs to be exercised, however, with any other herbs you might wish to administer, so check anything you are not sure of with a qualified herbalist before giving it to your horse. If your horse is undergoing veterinary treatment for any serious condition, it is also advisable to check with the vet and a herbalist before adding herbs you might not be sure about to the mix.

If a nutritional scientist were to analyze the herbs recommended for use in these pages, he would find they contain useful amounts of vitamins and minerals but, in most cases, he would conclude that they would stack up poorly in quantitative terms against artificially formulated supplements. He would conclude there is not enough calcium or phosphorous or iron or vitamin E, for example, to match the recommended daily averages his science has specified.

When it comes to dosage, there is not only disagreement between herbalists and conventional practitioners but, to further complicate matters, there are also various schools of thought within herbalism. These can be loosely grouped into adherents of: the physical dose, the trigger dose and the homeopathic dose. The detailed arguments between the three groups need not concern us here but, for your interest, the following comments will help before we get on with our business.

The Physical Dose

The physical-dose school of thought in herbal medicine tries to measure and administer the amount of individual ingredients in each herb known to have positive effects on health – in the same way as pharmaceutical companies. This means that their aim is to get the physical quantity of certain substances contained in the herb, which they see as being the active ingredients, to match up with pharmacological requirements.

Trying to fit a physical dose of a herbal medicine into the nutritional framework of 'recommended daily averages' simply does not work, because there is nothing more different than the functioning of one horse's metabolism as compared to another. Assuming that all horses require a certain fixed amount of this or that vitamin, mineral or nutritional substance is nonsense because, as we have seen, the aim is to treat the whole, *individual* horse, not some idea of the 'average' horse.

When looking at the health picture of a horse, we need to consider as a minimum:

• the whole picture of dietary, medical and work history;

- the present health and metabolic efficiency;
- the nervous-system;
- the individual animal's instinctive requirements, which will vary from day to day and season to season.

A careful evaluation of all the above factors would need to be taken into account to make these averages in any way 'scientific'. Basically, the physical-dose herbalists end up having to prescribe very large doses to make their numbers fit and, in the end, it simply defies common sense.

The Homeopathic Dose

This school of thought can be seen as diametrically opposed to the former, where homeopaths administer minuscule doses of certain herbs and substances to treat illness and imbalance. Homeopaths are very scientific in their own way and aim to match the very specific substances and potencies to reverse the processes of illness precisely (see Chapter 9: Herbs and the Other Therapies), and a very good and experienced homeopath has awesome power to set such reversals in motion.

Even the homeopath, however, concedes that other management factors and feeding requirements must also form part of any rehabilitation. He often ends up with herbal and other common-sense suggestions to accompany his treatments.

The Trigger Dose

Adherents of the trigger dose (the premise on which this book is based) know that often very small doses indeed of the correct herbs are all that is required for healing. It has been proven time and time again that small amounts of the correct herbal (or any other substances) trigger positive changes to take place in metabolic balances, digestion, excretion, immune- and nervous-system responses, and these result in healing. Of course, this also defies conventional scientific measurement. But then, trying to turn the art of healing into a science is simply a waste of time.

The old timers would say that a handful of herbs is a proper dose for a horse – just as a teaspoon of dried herbs in a cup of boiling water is the proper dose for a human cup of tea – and this seems to be true. If you watch your horse seeking herbs and 'weeds' along the side of the road or in the hedgerow you will see him taking a little of this and a little of that, in quite small quantities usually. He certainly does not ingest serious quantities as when you watch him eating grain or hay in his stall, or out in good fresh green pasture.

For those new to herbalism, suggested dose amounts for herbs may seem somewhat inexact. However, when dealing with herbs, it is not necessary (and is in fact counterproductive) for the herbalist to attempt to be too 'scientific'. What is important is that the horse receives the appropriate herb regularly in small amounts.

Often the commercially prescribed quantities are much more than the horse needs. This is to make the owner feel happy with what seems to him to be a respectable amount. How would you feel, for example, if the directions on the box of dried kelp said that a quarter of a teaspoon every couple of days is more than enough!

Throughout the remainder of the book, various herbs will be recommended for various conditions and, in some cases, specific instructions on preparation are included. However, once you know what herb/s your horse needs, there are various options in administering the herb. It may be possible to allow him access to the fresh herbs from a herbal hedgerow; to add fresh or dried herbs to his daily feed rations; to make a tea from the dried herbs/seeds; to add a vinegar extract (obtained from a herbalist or home-made) to the horse's feed or water; or you may have to have a specific mixture made up by a professional herbalist.

The following sections deal with doses and duration of treatment for the various forms in which you will feed herbs to your horse, and general instructions for preparation follow.

Doses for Dry Herb Mixes

The standard dose for dry herb mixes is one cupful (a handful if you wish), irrespective of the number of herbs included in the mix, twice a day mixed in with the horse's daily feeds morning and night.

This dose is to be continued until the progress of healing is obvious, when the dose can often be reduced to a half cup twice a day. Treatment should be continued for at least six to twelve weeks beyond the disappearance of all symptoms.

Above: Dried herbs mixed in feed

Left: Handful of dried red clover

Making Herbal Teas

The usual daily dose for herbal teas is two heaped tablespoons of seeds, or a quarter to a half a cup of dried herb.

Step 1

Measure out the quantity of the dried herb/s you are intending to feed your horse into a 2 liter jug.

Boiling water being added to tea

Step 2
Pour over one 1 liter of boiling water and allow the tea to stand until cool.

Step 3
This dose is then divided into two equal amounts and fed to the horse half in the morning and half at night, including the herb material with the tea.

Herb tea being made   Herb tea standing

Making fresh-herb tea in a bucket

Herbal teas can be refrigerated and stored for a few days but, in general, it is better to make up the next day's supply the night before and let it steep and cool overnight.

As with dried herbal mixes, herbal teas should be given until the progress of healing is obvious and treatment should be continued for at least six to twelve weeks beyond the disappearance of all symptoms. Then, occasional doses should be given as part of the particular horse's regular program once any specific tea has proven to be beneficial. Extra doses can also be given at times of stress, competition or heavy workload.

Making Molasses Extracts

To make herbs more palatable (and, as we have seen, to preserve them), various parts of fresh herbs can simply be stuffed into a drum of molasses. The oils from the herbs seep into the molasses and horses will willingly (in most cases enthusiastically) eat molasses in their feed.

Just tear or cut leaves or flowers into smallish pieces, or clean and chop up and submerge them in the sticky mass. After a couple of days simply add a cupful of the resulting mixture to the horse's feed. A very effective worming extract of wormwood leaves and garlic cloves is made in this manner.

Above: Garlic and wormwood extract in molasses

Left: Mixing molasses into feed by hand

Doses of Vinegar Extracts

Vinegar extracts vary in strength and it is not possible to match in concentration the 1:1 (equal quantities of herb/s and alcohol) alcohol-based extracts usually formulated to treat canine and human patients. My vinegar extracts are typically 1:6 (one part herb/s to six parts vinegar) to 1:10, and will contain six or so main herbs, with perhaps a couple of others in smaller amounts.

The amounts to administer are 10 or 20 ml of these extracts twice a day mixed into water or herbal tea and used to dampen feed. Alternatively, these doses can be given over the tongue via an empty worming syringe or a drench gun. Most horses quickly come to enjoy the taste of vinegar and there is rarely a need to force them to take the mixture. Duration of treatment is the same as for herbal teas.

In all cases of treatment the horse should be free to exercise and to socialize within sensible limits. He should have free access to fresh green pasture, and should be put back into light work as soon as the symptoms of illness begin to subside.

Herbal Blends

It is not recommended to use herbal medicines made of single herbs; this is too much like the 'quick fix' or 'this herb is good for that named disease'. A horse in nature does not dose on single herbs but grazes from the seasonal smorgasbord to maintain and restore health. This situation is what we are trying to recreate.

Blending between four and six different herbs together usually means that the complementary activity of all the ingredients within each herb and their support for one another will work as nature intended. It is not even necessary to understand exactly how they are working, just that they do. The chapter dealing with specific conditions (Chapter 10) lists a variety of herbs that will work together to restore wellbeing.

Feeding Hints

In general, your horse's herbal mix can be added to his feed ration morning and night. For the horses not receiving regular hard feeds, make up a bran mash (2-3 3 liter scoops of good quality bran, dampened to a 'crumbly' consistency with molasses mixed into warm water) and add the herbal mixture. You can also syringe the mix into the horse's mouth over his tongue. The teas or vinegar mixes can also be added to the horse's water but only if he has individual water, finds the mix palatable and if you can monitor that he has drunk the entire contents of his water container.

Most horses find the herbal mixes very palatable, so getting them to ingest them is rarely a problem.

Tips and Traps

There are two 'traps' for someone new to the herbal field, one of which is fairly acceptable common practice, the other of which is to be avoided. Also there are some possible reactions of which to be aware and some safety considerations to bear in mind before treating your horse herbally.

The 'Buckshot' Approach

As you read up on each of the herbs and as you get to know them, you will become more and more confused because of the multiple actions and uses ascribed to each of them. You will find, for example, that vervain in a recent herbal book is cited as good 'to help strengthen and restore the nervous system particularly after illness, for any liver complaints, to promote milk production, to help with mouth ulcers and with inflammation of the eyes'. (This is just a rewrite of the actions in plain English.) Now this seems to be fairly helpful on the surface, but when you read a bigger book you get a bigger list. It is not too long before you have a large number of herbs – all of which are 'good for the nervous system' or 'good for the liver' or 'good for the breeding mare'. The question is: how do we choose from among them?

This overload of information often leads to the 'buckshot' approach in herbal medicine. This involves putting all the herbs you can think of for, for example, the liver, in a single mix or pill, closing your eyes and hoping for the best. This approach can work to some extent but is not as effective as individually formulated treatment.

This is the approach used in the formulation of many health-food store and proprietary herbal 'medicines'. If there are more than six or eight herbs on a list of ingredients of a proprietary herbal mixture to treat a specific condition, this is a buckshot mix made up by an amateur.

There are important ingredients missing from the off-the-shelf buckshot approach – not the least being the observer's intentions and the interaction of the energies between the practitioner and the patient. Herbal medicine operates on the premise that we are not 'what we eat' but a combination of what we eat and the love and care put into the preparation of what goes into our mouths (ask any good cook), along with the compassion and intentions in preparing and administering formulations. As we all know, the scientific approach has no way of understanding any system that is other than mechanistic and we and our animals as living creatures are far, far more than that.

When starting out, it is perfectly acceptable to use combinations of many herbs known to be useful in certain conditions, as long as they are used with care, knowledge and the right intention. As you acquire more knowledge about herbs and develop a feel for the way in which herbs operate on the various body systems, you will be able to narrow down the right herbs for the job at hand – this skill comes with practice and time. Following sections will provide a good starting point, and also make suggestions to help you in refining your knowledge.

'More is Better'

When someone is starting out with herbs, in addition to the buckshot approach they are often tempted to use the 'more is better' approach, which is based on the assumption that if a little of something is good for you then more must be better. This is a much more dangerous practice, and is to be avoided.

There is a fundamental law in herbal medicine that states if a little of a particular substance produces one effect in the body; too much of the same substance will produce the opposite effect. A few carrots as a treat for your horse provides an excellent source of vitamin A and many other vitamins and minerals; a sack full of carrots in a single feed will probably cause vitamin A poisoning and liver damage (read the section on oats in the materia medica).

In fact, the whole science of homeopathy (which we deal with later as a valuable complementary therapy to use with herbs) is based around this very principal – but applied in the opposite manner. For example, if one of the main symptoms of strychnine poisoning is muscular contractions of the stomach and solar plexus, then tiny, tiny doses of the same substance can be made into homeopathic medicines to relieve a patient afflicted by similar contractions. This remedy is known as nux vomica, and is made by extreme dilution of a tincture of the deadly Indian poison nut – the crushed seeds of which contain about 5% strychnine and other poisonous substances.

From the herbal perspective, the 'more is better' is at best an unnecessarily expensive, and at worst a dangerous, approach that is to be avoided.

Reactions

Very rarely, a horse may seem to 'react' to the initial introduction of herbs to his diet. A reaction is usually an indication that the horse's metabolism, while desperately needing some ingredient found in the herb, will react as to an overdose with initial contact. This response is tested by a brief interruption of the herbal treatment and resumption at a smaller dose, which is then built up. The reaction almost never recurs.

Sometimes the horse's original symptoms may very occasionally seem to worsen. If this happens, simply cease feeding the herbs for a few days, and then restart at half the dose.

Occasionally also, the horse's coat may change color and in this case the owner needs to assess whether the coat is simply looking healthier after the introduction of the herbs (the usual, desirable, scenario), or is just different. Usually if this is a simple initial change of color, the coat will change back after a short time.

If there is a change in the horse's stool after the introduction of his herbal mix, the best approach is usually to watch and wait and add chamomile tea to dampen down his feed. Herbs are very unlikely to produce serious scours but, if this seems to be the case, stop feeding the herbs for a few days and replace them with a cup of slippery elm powder mixed into a paste with chamomile tea, and five drops of Bach Flower Rescue Remedy (available from health-food shops – see Chapter 9: Homeopathy and Bach Flowers for further information) twice daily in the interim.

The rule of thumb in watching for reactions is to note any deviation from what is normal for that particular horse and to assess the importance of these deviations. Any undesirable reactions are very unlikely, while desirable reactions are very likely. Naturally, any continuing concerns should be addressed to a professional herbalist or your vet.

A Note on Safety

Although there are no safety and dose concerns with the 'do-it-yourself' mixes recommended in this book (unless they are flagged with a caution comment), there are other herbs that must be approached with care. So, if you are intending to treat your horse herbally with anything other than the herbs and doses advocated in this book, you are well advised to seek the advice of a professional herbalist.

3 Growing Herbs

Most of the herbs we use are considered by many people (and agricultural authorities) to be 'weeds', which means they are not difficult to grow. Far from being hothouse flowers, herbs are hardy plants that will usually thrive in the right conditions.

Many people set aside designated herb gardens and expend much time and effort creating and maintaining these. If you happen to be an avid gardener, then herbs will thrive in a designated garden or among other garden plants (in fact the judicious planting of herbs around ornamentals and vegetables can enhance their health and make spraying for pests unnecessary).

If you are not a gardener and just want to grow the basic herbs for your family's and animals' health, this need not be a major undertaking. Herbs can be grown from seedlings (available from specialist and many standard nurseries), from seeds, and some will grow from cuttings or division. As is the case with all plants: some like shade; some like sun; some like to be kept damp; others thrive in the dry. Seek the advice of the nursery on the best places to plant your herbs and read the accompanying labels.

Some herbs are perennial, others will die down and reseed – in which case it is a good idea to collect some seeds for planting next season. Seeds are also available to you if you are already buying them to feed to your horse, e.g. whole rosehips simply planted in the ground and watered will give you wild dog-rose bushes.

The main thing to remember with herbs is that, in the main, they are hardy plants that do not require a lot of tending, which makes them perfect plants to grow in hedgerows – the ideal way to cultivate them on horse properties.

Herbal Hedgerows

The very best way to use herbs for health and wellbeing, as we have seen, is for your horse to self-medicate as his instincts dictate. Most of us do not have access to huge tracts of untouched land for our horses to roam, so hedgerows are the next best things. Creating herbal hedgerows (called 'ditches' in Ireland) around your property, will allow your horses access to those plants they would forage for in the wild and also provide a place to grow herbs for drying and collection for your supplement program, or for the treatment of specific problems.

The best base for a hedgerow is the hawthorn bush. Not only is an extract of fresh hawthorn leaves or dried berries a major heart tonic and first-aid treatment for severe injury or illness, but the prickly plants are also

Hawthorn hedge

an ideal breeding ground for 'weeds' (herbs) – they protect the herbs from being grazed to the ground but make them available as required. The horse's instincts will cause him to put up with some discomfort (i.e. prickles on the nose) to get at something he desperately needs within the hawthorns, while the idle grazer will think twice about foraging in the prickles. How clever nature is!

It is a very simple matter to grow sections of hedges at the intersection of pastures – or even across pastures – as wind breaks and shelters or as privacy hedges. Not only will the hedges serve as the base for your medicinal herbs, but these hedges will also provide protection for your horses from wind, rain and cold (which means they will need less feed); they will protect pasture from the ravages of the elements and will also help to prevent erosion in your pastures (and pockets). As an added bonus, a mature hedge creates a wildlife corridor for birds, insects and even small mammals by providing perfect protected nesting sites, food and shelter.

Hedgerows in the UK

Place a water trough up against the hedgerow at some point, with an overflow or sprinkler part-way along the hedge. This will allow for a damper environment for some of the herbs – like borage, chickweed, comfrey, mint and parsley, for example, which prefer this sort of situation. Shovel manure up against some parts of your hedge and leave other parts very dry, in order to vary the environment as much as possible to cater for the different needs of the different herbs.

When you have the basic hedgerows planted, all you need to do is to seed the herbs within them; herbs really are usually very hardy and just require some watering in dry climates. Protect the whole hedge for a couple of seasons with an electric, post and rail, or net, fence and you have your own living 'supplement and treatment hedgerow'.

The Herb Garden

If herbal hedgerows are not a viable option for you, you can create a designated herb garden, and include herbs for your animals and yourself, as well as culinary herbs. If you situate this close to the stables - perhaps with a vegetable garden for company – the herbs will be easily accessible for adding to feed, and the horse manure will be easily accessible for recycling as fertilizer.

Above: Herbs grown in a greenhouse

Above right and right: Hambledon herbs, Somerset, UK

Southern Light herbs, Victoria, Australia

Greenfarm herbs

Old car tires make wonderful planting pots for individual herbs and are great for those herbs with a propensity to take over the whole garden – mints for example. You can stack the tires at different levels, fill them with soil and manure, and plant herbs (and vegetables) both inside and outside the tires for an easy, effective landscaping job. The design options are endless and limited only by your imagination.

Choosing Herbs

When choosing the herbs to grow, try to find seeds from an herb nursery, or if you are lucky enough to have friends with established herb gardens, have them collect seeds (or cuttings) from their herbs for you.

Above: Dandelion seed plot

Right: Garlic plot

If you buy seedlings from a nursery (herbs grow so fast, tubes are usually the best and most economical way to buy them), make sure you buy healthy, vigorous plants for the best chance of success. Check that the leaves and foliage on the plants are healthy (not browned, mottled, or discolored), that the root tips are not discolored, that any new shoots look lush and healthy, and that the stems are healthy looking, i.e. not discolored.

Your 'herbal mix' for growing (either in hedgerows or your herb garden) could include, but not be limited to, the following herbs:

aniseed, borage, comfrey, chamomile, dandelion, dill, equisetum (horsetail), fennel, garlic, horehound, horseradish, hypericum (St Johns wort), millet, mint, nettle, parsley, pennyroyal, red clover, rosehips, rosemary, rue, sage, St Mary's thistle, shepherds purse, thyme, tansy, vervain, wild lettuce, wormwood and yarrow.

Parsley rows

Rue garden

Thyme plot

When selecting the individual herbs, you need to find the wild varieties, not the modern commercial ones. That is to say, find some of the old-fashioned garlic with the small cloves and make sure you get the wild or dog rose with the small pink flowers and not the commercial ornamental roses.

PART 2
Herbs and
the Horse

4 Herbs for General Health

There are certain broad health and wellbeing areas where the use of herbs is an extremely effective and non-invasive alternative to conventional veterinary treatments. Many of the drugs we have given our animals, and ourselves as we have already seen, are causing severe side effects and repercussions. If we can substitute herbs and other natural treatments for chemicals, we are well on the road to having a horse with a balanced metabolism, which is not ticking away as a 'health time-bomb'.

So, we are now thinking of the illness holistically in terms of the horse's body processes and we are thinking of herbs in terms of their overall properties and the way in which each of them support these bodily processes. You are now ready to choose, prepare and administer herbs for specific purposes.

We will just quickly review again the underlying assumptions, and then get on with the business of treating your horse.

Treating the Whole Horse

The difference between holistic or naturopathic medicine and orthodox medicine is basically the overall approach. The natural therapies treat the individual patient – human or animal – as a whole being, and aim to achieve a balance and harmony in all the systems and the whole environment of that being. This is the basis of good health: balancing the body's systems so they operate in optimum harmony with the physical and emotional environment in which it lives and functions.

Orthodox medicine just looks at fragments (individual symptoms and illnesses as separate entities) and usually omits any consideration of the whole person or animal in their personal environment. It becomes a series of 'sticking-plaster solutions' to cover up symptoms of imbalance, which, if ignored long enough, usually lead to a serious breakdown in health.

Orthodox medicine, in contrast to herbalism, is committed to the 'magic bullet' notion; name the condition 'headache', for example, and find a substance that 'fixes' headaches. Some clever chemist (after talking to the natives) extracted a few chemical ingredients (salicylates actually) from the bark of the white willow tree. He then learned how to make them artificially, patented the process, called it aspirin, and the modern pharmaceutical age began.

Modern medicine became committed to taking away or masking ('alleviating' they say on the packets) the symptoms of illness. In doing so they gave up on the idea of understanding and assisting the body to reverse the processes of ill health that led to the appearance of the symptoms. This is the 'magic bullet' or 'quick fix' approach, and this has caused many of the health problems facing recent generations of humans and their domestic animals.

Herbs, on the other hand, are used to balance, nourish and restore, and are therefore better understood in terms of their effects on the systems of the body and not in terms of named diseases. Understanding this is the first big hurdle toward naturopathic or holistic thinking.

Because our aim in treating the whole horse is to consider his whole mental and physical environment, in most instances throughout the book we refer not only to herbal treatments, but make other suggestions in terms of management practices. Herbal support for the body processes; natural feeding, shoeing, and dentistry practices; keeping horses in circumstances that closely resemble their natural state; following 'horse friendly', varied and non-violent starting and training regimens: all of these factors have a large bearing on the horse's wellbeing. Throughout the following sections we allude to common-sense management practices as part of the total treatment but, because feeding is a major consideration for most horse owners, we have added the following comments as general guidelines.

Feeding Practices

Prepared horse feed undoubtedly contributes to weaknesses in the modern horse. This is because, although their chemical balances are all very carefully worked out and shown on the packages, the individual ingredients that are blended to create these balances are often not natural feed substances for horses, or not in the balance found in nature, and are therefore poorly metabolized.

Also, while it is possible to see if a particular batch of natural feed is not right by its look, smell or feel, it is much more difficult to tell if the ingredients of prepared feeds were fresh or healthy when they were ground, blended and made into pellets. Then, of course, once you crush a grain, you break down its protective shell and the goodness diminishes very quickly. It is far better to keep the feed as natural and unprocessed as possible.

It is important, if possible, to buy feed that is grown free of chemical sprays and in pastures that have nutritionally balanced soil (unfortunately a very rare commodity in many parts of the world). A good general rule of thumb in selecting feed is to bear in mind that the more processed a feed product is, the less value it has nutritionally and the more costly it is to buy. For example alfalfa (lucerne) hay (relatively inexpensive, high nutrition value, high in fiber) becomes chaff (more expensive, less long fiber), which is compressed into pellets (more expensive again and usually with additives). Try to stick to whole, chemical-free, natural products if you can.

Bran has long been considered a good staple food for horses, but there has been some debate over recent years about the advisability of feeding it because modern bran (made from wheat) bears little resemblance to old-fashioned 'broad bran'. However, bran still provides some nutrients, roughage, and a palatable way – when made into a mash with molasses – to get a horse to eat feed additives. The caution with bran these days, as with any other foodstuffs, is to seek out the best quality, chemical-free product possible. Bran also needs to be fresh – not a stale product that has been sitting around a storeroom for many months. Smelling the product will again give you a fair indication of the quality and freshness – if it smells at all stale or musty, return it immediately to the supplier. Where bran is mentioned in this book, we mean the best quality, freshest flaky bran you can obtain – not other inferior grain by-products, which can cause gut impactions.

Where possible, give your horse the opportunity to seek out what he needs. If a horse is confined to a small area, or kept in 'clean' pastures that are free of 'weeds', an excellent practice is to take him for a walk on a long lead, and allow him to seek out all the herbs and grasses he needs along the roadsides.

As a general rule, do not over care! Love your horses by all means and work them hard – but do not feed them hard! Remember that a section of lovely fresh lucerne hay or a small dollop of honey is an appropriate treat for a horse – nothing more processed or more exotic than this. Having saturated the world markets with snack foods for humans, the junk food companies are now looking toward snack foods for animals – so far mostly cats and dogs. Recently we have seen a few snack foods for horses appearing in the marketplace. Do not buy into it!

The basic diet

In general, a good, simple, basic diet for a horse is alfalfa (lucerne), meadow or oaten hay and oats. Along with a little fresh green pasture, these three feed substances will provide the bulk, vitamins, minerals, protein and energy your horse will require. No one really argues that alfalfa or meadow or oaten hay are not suitable feed for a horse, but we do often hear that oats are too 'heating' and should be replaced by one or other of the pelletized (made into pellets) 'cooler' grain preparations. It may be true that some horses, confined to stables or small yards with little outlet for their energy, might be made too 'hot' by large doses of oats. However, this should not be an argument to deny such an ideal source of carbohydrates, protein and energy to every horse on earth. There is an appropriate amount of oats for every horse and this will depend on their individual nature, metabolism, circumstances and workload (bearing in mind that, in the wild, a horse would only eat a small proportion of grain to stalk, so the feed should be mainly roughage). All a horse owner needs to do is identify the appropriate amount of oats for the individual horse based on first-hand knowledge of his temperament and circumstances, and perhaps soak or crush the oats before blending with a suitable amount of dried feed.

In herbal medicine, as you will see shortly, oats are a nervine and are particularly suitable to nourish a nervous-system type that will work hard, honestly and patiently day after day, week after week and year after year. This is surely the basic nature of a horse, which makes small amounts of oats the perfect feed.

Now, on to the practical application of herbs. In the day-to-day caring for our horses, the following areas respond well to the use of herbal preparations.

Nerve Tonics

These days, a large number of performance horses are highly strung to the point where it impedes their performance and, in some cases, makes the animal dangerous. Many riders and trainers have resorted to the use of chemical sedatives and tranquilizers to calm their horses but, not only are these products often illegal to use in competitive situations, they can also damage the horse's overall health and wellbeing. Judiciously used herbs are a far better alternative for treating the nervous horse as they often effect a permanent change in temperament and are 'legal' for competition.

Herbs nourish, strengthen and rebalance the nervous system so that once an anxious horse calms down he no longer over-reacts to his environment. The actions of sedatives and tranquilizers on the horse's nervous system are completely different: they simply block nervous-system responses for as long as the drug remains in the horse's system. This is why they are a 'one-time fix' instead of an overall cure. The right herb will mean the nervous horse will no longer want to shy, buck, rear, 'freeze' or bolt and the rebalancing with the right herbs is usually permanent.

In dealing with nervous disorders, there are no magic quick fixes. In treating a horse that has a nervous temperament, it is very important to look at the horse's whole history – both health and past experiences – such as training, traumas, etc. This gives us the information to combine herbs and other treatments – such as homeopathy, nutrition, and perhaps even a change in training regimen or routine – to bring the horse's whole metabolism back into balance.

Treating the whole horse rather than a specific nervous disorder is important because there is a very close relationship between how a nervous system reacts and responds, and how the horse's whole metabolism functions.

Nervines

While we stress that it is not advisable to attempt to treat a horse with a severe nervous problem without professional advice, if a horse's nervousness is due to a slight imbalance, feeding him a mix of herbs will usually effect a long-term solution.

There is a class of herbs called 'nervines', i.e. herbs that have specific actions on the nervous system. Many of the nervines contain high levels of magnesium phosphate – a mineral that has been found to be very important to the health and wellbeing of nerves. Different nervines nourish different aspects of the nervous system; the job of the herbalist is to identify the nervine(s) that will suit a particular sort of nervous system.

There are around a dozen nervines that apply to humans, but there are four main nervines – valerian, vervain, chamomile, and hops – that apply to horses. A horse will not always fit exactly into just one nervous-system type – he will often show the major signs of one type, and some signs of one or more of the other types. The first step in finding the right herbs to treat your horse's nervous disorder is to identify his nervous 'type/s'.

The Types

The **valerian** horse typically holds all his anxiety and tension in his muscles: you will find his muscles will always be a little taut. When frightened, this horse will literally become rigid with fear, with the muscles all rock-hard. He is the horse in the western trail event that appears on the surface to be managing the obstacles but his teeth are grinding and the rider can feel the rigid tension beneath the saddle. He is the kind of horse you often see at shows, where he makes it (albeit somewhat stiffly!) around the dressage arena accompanied by the sound of teeth gnashing on the bit. While the valerian horse typically freezes up with his tension rather than spooking or bolting, if he encounters a series of stressful events, he may just explode – bucking, rearing or taking off.

The herb valerian is popularly used to help people with sleeping problems, and the application to horses is similar. Even in relatively low-stress situations, the valerian type of horse has a hard time truly relaxing his muscles. In its application to the nervous horse, valerian relaxes and rebalances the nervous system so the horse is able to relax muscular tension.

The **vervain** horse's anxiety is processed through the skin. He is very sensitive and twitchy on the skin and is generally very nervous and jumpy, without necessarily being afraid, upset or angry. This is the horse that is constantly agitated and highly reactive, always moving and fidgeting. Sometimes it seems it is almost impossible to make this horse stand still, and he is the equine equivalent of a person who constantly taps a foot or chews on his or her fingernails.

Training methods that rely on repetitive exposure to frightening situations to reduce the 'spook' in a horse will often backfire with a horse of this temperament. This type is very common among horses who have raced or those of race breeding as the successful fast runner has been bred to have excess energy that often presents as this fidgety temperament. The vervain horse is also more likely to become a crib-biter, weaver or wind-sucker when kept in a confined space for lengthy periods as developing these vices provides an outlet for his excess energy.

Giving this horse the herb vervain rebalances his nervous system so that he stops the endless fidgeting, moving and jumpiness. This horse will always be sensitive yet, once his nervous-system health returns, he will be able to slow down and concentrate, making him more trainable and therefore more reliable under pressure.

The **chamomile** horse's anxiety is processed through his digestive system. He gets upset easily, almost always presenting with diarrhea or scours when he is nervous or worried. He may show some signs of external stress (like the other nervine types above) but he mainly internalizes his worry so, while he may be a little spooky, the chamomile horse's main problems are in the gut. The chamomile horse may even suffer an attack of colic when under stress, and he is the one that rapidly loses weight and coat condition in stressful situations. He is the racehorse that will go off his feed after a race and take three weeks of work and feeding before he is ready to race at his best again.

Treating the chamomile nervous-system type horse with this herb chamomile not only rebalances the nervous system, but also helps to maintain the health of the horse's digestive system.

The **hops** horse processes his anxiety through his head. He is easily distracted mentally, and it is very difficult for him to concentrate because he is constantly very scattered and unfocused. These horses are the 'dizzy-lizzies' of the horse world. He is usually very 'busy' in the head, although not necessarily physically 'hot' to handle and ride. He will be difficult to train in the sense that he will not retain things well. With the hops horse, you will find yourself going over the same issues again and again, and his concentration span often seems to be less than thirty seconds.

Giving him the herb hops allows him to calm down mentally and to become focused. In this balanced state, the hops horse will be able to concentrate on the job at hand and, given the right direction, he can shine in his chosen field.

Oats, which were mentioned in the previous section, are also a nervine that have proved to be very valuable in human herbal practice. For humans, oats are a valuable tonic for the physically hard–working, 'stoic' sort of individual who has become run down and whose health is suffering due to prolonged overwork. This is why a bowl of rolled oaten porridge is sufficient to do a half-day of hard physical work in a cold climate. Try doing a half-day's fencing on a bowl of breakfast cereal!

For horses, oats must therefore be seen as both a feed and as a medicine. If you do find difficulty determining the correct amount of oats to feed your particular horse, you might like to try one tablespoon of oats made into an herbal tea (see Chapter 2: Making Herbal Teas), and give this twice a day.

Passion flower is another herb that has proved to be very effective in treating long-standing nervous habits, but it is usually administered in conjunction with other nervines. Passion flower helps to relax the nervous system and works particularly well (almost as a catalyst) in conjunction with one or more of the preceding herbs to facilitate the effect of the 'primary herbs'.

There is not really a passion-flower type, but the herb acts as a facilitator that helps the horse to set aside previously entrenched reaction patterns and adopt newer more comfortable patterns. Passion flower would be appropriate for the ex-racehorse type, or indeed any horse that has a long history of nervous or 'temperament' problems: the persistently spooky horse; the long-time bucker/rearer/bolter, for example.

Passion flower's chief asset is that it assists in the breaking of nervous-system habit patterns as opposed to normalizing a particular nervous-system type. It is almost always used in conjunction with the dominant nervine.

Hypericum or **St Johns wort** is another nervine that has some application as a nervous-system type but is best used in support of specific treatments, externally and in small and regulated doses internally. The actions of hypericum are described more fully in the materia medica toward the end of the book.

Feeding the Mix

Once a horse's nervous-system type (or in some cases types) is identified, giving him the corresponding herb or combination of herbs will usually correct the imbalance and end the nervous behavior.

Once you have identified his nervous type/s, make up a herbal tea for your horse from the herb/s you have decided he needs, using the instructions described in Making Herbal Teas in Chapter 2. Give him half the daily dose of tea in his morning feed and the other half in his night feed – including the herbal material with the liquid and mixing well into the feed.

Treatment with the appropriate herb or herbs needs to take place daily for around three months. While a really obvious change in behavior usually occurs in the first month, if the proper herbs are used for the full course of treatment, a permanent change can occur. You may need to experiment a little with the different nervines to get the right herb or combination of herbs for your nervous horse; changes in behavior and attitude will tell you the right combination.

The herbs work by allowing the horse to relax and removing the need for nervous reactions. This re-educates the nervous system as it settles into new habits, so that the horse no longer reacts in the old way.

Sometimes, after a year or so following a treatment course, a horse may revert to old behavior patterns as a result of his nervous system becoming unbalanced. This reversion could be due to stress resulting from a change in his physical environment (a new owner/home), strenuous performance demands, an accident, surgery, or feeding/medicating with chemicals and, almost always, a month or so follow-up with his particular mix will correct the problem.

Sometimes, however, you will find a horse that needs to be given his particular herb/s indefinitely but this horse is the exception. These horses may have long, ingrained behavior patterns, a history of abuse, or other metabolic problems that continue to upset the balance of the nervous system. These are cases to be dealt with by professional herbalists.

Also, if a horse's nervous system is seriously out of balance, there will be physiological implications – such as inefficient digestion or absorption, inability to hold condition, hormonal imbalances and structural weakness – all of which must be addressed in conjunction with the nervous system by a professional in order to effect a complete return to normal. For example, a severe imbalance or nervous-system disorder can affect the horse's digestive efficiency, thyroid balance, liver function, respiratory efficiency, blood quality and immunity to infection. These aspects of the horse's metabolism must all be brought into balance in order for a treatment of serious nervous-system problems to be truly effective and long lasting. This is where the advice of a professional herbalist is invaluable in prescribing a comprehensive treatment for each individual case.

Electrolytes

A widely practiced feeding supplementation is the routine adminis-tration of commercially prepared electrolytes to horses. From a holistic point of view, this is not a particularly good idea and there is an inexpensive, effective and health-giving natural alternative.

Salts

It is true that horses lose salts when they sweat. It is also true that there are quite a lot of vegetable salts in green and dried feed. In the wild, the horse's salt loss is balanced by what he is eating. Also, horses free to roam will seek out salt licks. Horses have highly refined instincts that will lead them to seek out salt when they need it.

The modern practice of giving horses specified amounts of electrolytes on a daily basis is subverting this natural instinct and forcing salt on the animal whether he needs it or not. This can never be as good as letting the horse's instincts decide how much salt he needs and when he needs it.

The best thing you can do for your horse in this area is to provide a natural rock-salt block (most stock feeders will get them in for you) or free access to a container of sea salt (from any health-food shop) for him to lick in the stable or in the yard. Then let him choose for himself.

Kelp

In addition to natural salts, it is also a good idea to give your horse access to seaweed as part of his diet – just dried giant kelp (bladderack), which you can collect after storms on beaches or purchase in powdered or granular form. If you can find dried clumps of kelp or granules rather than the powdered variety available at most stock feeders, this will avoid loss from wind, or the horse blowing on it as he self-medicates. Just keep it in a container in the horse's stall or yard and allow him to eat what he needs.

If a horse can 'free graze' on kelp, this will help to take care of his electrolyte needs, while at the same time he will be able to self-administer trace elements, which are all found in the seaweed.

Seaweed is a cellular feeder, which means that it absorbs directly from the seawater into the cells. Therefore, every cell contains everything – selenium, gold, arsenic, copper – you name it, it is there. The exact function of only a few trace elements is known (e.g. the role of iodine in thyroid health), but what is known is that even extremely minute amounts of these elements are very important indeed to animals and humans. The point is, we do not need to know (and maybe never will) exactly what a horse needs, and it does not matter. Any such imbalance will be corrected by allowing him free access to kelp and any excess will be excreted naturally.

However, bear in mind that there are probably not enough electrolytes in kelp to serve as the sole source because the horse will instinctively limit the amount of kelp to what he requires in terms of trace elements. Access to sea salt or salt blocks make up the shortfall.

Self-medication

The idea of allowing the horse to self-medicate is a sound practice, as he instinctively knows what he needs on a daily basis. This in turn saves on wastage because he will just excrete what he does not need if you mix the additives into his feed – often making it an expensive exercise as your money goes in one end and out the other!

A permanent tray with compartments (like those used in cutlery drawers or toolboxes for example) could be attached somewhere under the eaves of the stable or the horse's shade structure. This could contain sea salt in one compartment, kelp in another and, say, dolomite (another important nutritional component containing magnesium and calcium in a naturally balanced formulation) in another.

You do not need to worry about the amount of these substances you give the horse, just keep the compartments topped up. You will be surprised to note the different requirements of different horses and, even more interesting, is the different requirements on different days of the same horse.

It is far healthier and more economical to allow each individual horse's instinct to work and to learn for yourself about their individual requirements. You will also be alerted by changes in demand as to the emergence of possible health problems before they become serious.

Performance

Electrolytes are routinely given in increased amounts to performance horses on hot days and after strong exertion. There is a natural alternative to this. If you are following the regimen outlined above, do not change this on the days of the competition or event, just keep the salt and the kelp available and keep up the fluids to the horse.

In addition to this, a really valuable practice in minimizing the stress of competition and exertion is to give the horse rosehips tea on the day before, during and after competition: two tablespoons of the granulated herb steeped in 1 liter of hot water, cooled and added to feed or water at least twice a day.

Allergies and Blood Cleansing

Skin conditions caused by allergic reactions are endemic in domestic animals these days and horses are no exception. Orthodox veterinary medicine has fallen short in providing any long-term solution for the increasing number of animals suffering skin allergies, while the alternative therapies – in particular herbal remedies – are proving beneficial in understanding and treating these conditions.

In a horse with a highly sensitive digestive and/or immune system (and this is extremely common in domestic horses), the blood is constantly being subjected to quality changes as a result of all this 'reactivity'. Such a horse is quickly classified as allergic as if this is some sort of an illness, rather than an over-enthusiastic immune system.

Often, as the condition develops, the accumulation of toxins shows up as lumps or cysts that form under the skin. These are actually caused by the immune system attempting to deal with toxins left behind in the blood as a result of the constant reactivity changes. These toxins, if not being carried out efficiently though the kidneys or bowel, are 'packaged' and stored just under the skin to keep them out of harm's way.

The natural resolution of this situation is that the toxic material can be released later through the skin via perspiration; reabsorbed into the lymphatic system and discharged through the bowel; or discharged by allowing a localized process of infection to develop, break through the skin and be expelled.

All these processes are within the repertoire of a healthy immune system and should preferably not be subverted by surgical intervention or by the use of antibiotic therapy but, rather, encouraged and allowed to run their natural course.

The Treatment Options

Orthodox veterinary medicine usually offers either desensitization programs or antibiotic therapy. Desensitizing injections further stress the immunity by introducing substances directly into the body without any prior warning, and each such injection administers a grave shock to the immune system (see page 99: Vaccinations and Injections). These programs are long, intrusive, expensive and of questionable value.

Antibiotic treatments deny the release through eruptions at the skin level and produce even more toxins in the blood, which add to the existent load. Again, antibiotics further stress the immune system if given by injection and decimate the gut flora, thus compromising digestive processes and further depleting the animal's vitality.

Following these two approaches often results in even more severe allergic responses, which lead to steroid treatments. By this time the horse is often quite ill and has caused the owner considerable expense with no real prospect of improvement.

Of course, some horses will improve due solely to their own fortitude and in spite of all this interference but surely less intrusive and more natural treatment for a better outcome would be desirable. The holistic approach is to calm and heal the nervous, digestive and immune systems and to facilitate the release of the toxins produced in the blood.

These processes are very simple and are best managed at home, on the advice of a herbalist (as some of the herbs must be used advisedly and with caution). They will often involve the use of herbal allergy mixes to address the sensitivity and histamine levels and many blood-cleansing or alterative herbs to clear the lymphatic system and assist in re-establishing the appropriate removal mechanisms.

Depending on the individual horse – his state of health and the extent the metabolism and immunity has been damaged along the way – sometimes further digestive, nervous-system and antioxidant programs are indicated as the treatment progresses are in order to bring all metabolic systems back to normal health. It is also usually advisable to address dietary or supplement intake to minimize the horse's exposure to chemical substances, which could have triggered excessive sensitivity in the first place.

Worming

Worms are a part of nature and a healthy gut in a horse can carry a small load of worms with few ill effects. It is even possible that in a healthy gut the worms play a supportive role in maintaining a balance but there is no doubt that heavy worm infestation in a horse can cause all sorts of health problems, not just confined to the gut. The worst scenario is death from worm-related colic.

There are three approaches to worming:

- The chemical drenches that kill worms more quickly than they kill horses, but they certainly do leave the animal less healthy.
- Worms can be anaesthetized and flushed out (which is how we deal with worms in humans) – a method which is preferable to chemically killing the worms.
- Herbal worming agents that work by dramatically toning up the health of the gut. They are also so bitter in taste that the worms no longer find the host suitable and depart.

The first step in dealing with worms is to follow a suitable land and pasture care regimen to promote healthy gastro-intestinal systems in your horses, which will minimize worm reinfestation. Pick up or plough manure in pastures regularly, rotate pastures (if possible with other stock such as cattle, because horse worms cannot live in cattle and therefore will not be able to complete their life cycle), and try to maintain a chemical-free environment.

The herbs you need to introduce regularly into your horses' diet are wormwood (surprise! surprise!) and garlic. A handful of fresh wormwood leaves stuffed into a cup of molasses (according to the instructions in Chapter 2: Making Molasses Extracts) makes a very healthy worming treatment that tones up the gut wall and makes the worms most uncomfortable. Garlic, either prepared the same way or fed fresh to the horses, will rapidly normalize the gut flora.

A full cup of a strong extract of fresh wormwood in molasses should be added to the horse's feed to begin treatment. This is best followed by a second dose twelve hours later – sometimes with a laxative in a severe case – and then another two doses after three weeks to pick up the next hatching of eggs. After this, a course of wormwood/molasses extract given every six weeks or so, and garlic every day or so will keep your horses well. If you were to take the time and trouble to have stool samples analyzed, you would notice the odd worm but you would not have a health-threatening worm infestation. Trying to kill every single worm in your horse's gut is impossible, debilitating and certainly not the way to optimum health.

Anti-inflammatories

Just as is the case with human health, the routine use (and often over-use) of anti-inflammatory drugs can have long-term ill effects and sometimes disastrous side effects on the health of our horses. There are a number of traditional herbal treatments that are very effective in treating pain and inflammation without the risks associated with chemicals.

Rheumatism, arthritis and pain resulting from accident, injury or over-exertion have been around as long as man and animals have walked upon the earth and the natural means to treat them have been around for just as long. The anti-inflammatory herbs were certainly not 'discovered' by scientists in a laboratory – in fact the anti-inflammatory properties of the bark of the white willow have been fully understood for all of mankind's recorded history.

Other herbs commonly referred to in the herbal writings of the Middle Ages (e.g. Culpepper's work written in Britain in the 1650s) were the herbs burdock, guaiacum, and devil's claw, all of which were recommended for the relief of rheumatism, arthritis and sciatica and all of which are used by herbalists for exactly the same complaints today.

The modern aspirin was 'discovered' simply by analyzing the bark of the white willow, and separating out one of the many medicinal ingredients. This ingredient was then synthesized, patented and promoted as the 'active ingredient' – and modern pharmaceutical companies were born. Aspirin is now being 'rediscovered' as a low-dose preventative/maintenance medicine now being prescribed as useful in preventing heart disease and improving circulation. (Hopefully it will not be long before doctors are prescribing white willow bark tea for the same purpose.)

With the age of the active ingredient came the age of the side effect. That is to say, while white willow bark extract even in quite high-dose levels and prolonged use has almost no effect on the gastro-intestinal tract, aspirin on the other hand, in even moderate doses and for relatively short periods, can cause ulceration, bleeding and worse in the stomach and the gut. Even in the low doses (100 mg) currently being prescribed in preventative medicine, there are emerging signs, particularly in many elderly people, that even these tiny doses are still too strong and cause digestive-system irritation and blood-vessel fragility.

The fact that aspirin use carries serious risks from side effects and that white willow bark does not, is simply because the package of complex chemical substances (dozens of them) present in the whole plant extract are excluded from the drug. It is this combination of substances – provided in its perfect form by nature – that meshes in a balanced and harmonious way with the complex chemistry of our bodily processes, which the singular active ingredient does not.

The modern practice of isolating the active ingredient is the problem. All ingredients in plant substances are 'active' and our bodies and those of our animals, which evolved on this earth with the plants, relate well to the packages and mostly not very well to the separate ingredients.

Routine usage of chemical medicines is almost always detrimental to long-term health prospects. This applies even to so-called 'safe' medications like aspirin and it applies much more to stronger ones like phenylbutazone ('bute'), which is arguably the most over-used drug given to horses. This drug can and does cause ulceration of the horse's digestive tract and severe scouring and, in severe cases, can result in death.

In looking at the way the horse's body heals itself, it is important to understand what happens in the case of a trauma or injury. Inflammation and pain are both part of the natural healing process: inflammation and swelling bring fluids to cushion a damaged area and aid in the healing process; pain will stop the horse causing further damage by continued use. When an animal is in pain he is meant to rest, not to continue with the activity causing the pain.

This brings us to the argument as to whether bute is dangerous to health and/or can mask pain sufficiently to allow your horse to continue work to the detriment of his long-term wellbeing. This obviously varies in individual cases, sensitivities and dose levels. In turn, this suggests that vets should be those best equipped to make these decisions and to control administration. Unfortunately, despite manufacturer's recommendations to the contrary, many individual owners administer their own bute. Most, but not all, phenylbutazone toxicity deaths and injury come as a complete surprise and are not due to massive overdoses but are simply the result of ignorance, careless dosing, or the particular horse's individual sensitivity.

As an alternative, there are combinations of anti-inflammatory herbs that reduce inflammation and pain, have no side effects, do not test positive to drug testing, and do not mask pain to the extent that the horse will continue with any level of work that will cause long-term damage to the injured area. In fact this can be taken a step further; these combinations include ingredients that reduce shock, promote healing, and clear the blood of toxic residues resulting from, or involved in, the pain process.

In an ideal situation, an herbalist will prepare individual mixes for individual horses, but there are some ingredients that are commonly used. A typical herbal treatment might include the following herbs: white willow bark and devil's claw as anti-inflammatory agents, guaiacum as a lubricant, and burdock as a blood cleanser for rheumatoid processes. All these herbs not only reduce inflammation and pain but also assist in the healing process, which in turn will help to reverse the underlying condition completely.

In our professional formulation we also include the herbs pine bark, rosehips, comfrey and yarrow, along with the Bach Flower Remedies honeysuckle, vine, walnut and Bach Flower Rescue Remedy in a formulation extracted into organic apple cider vinegar.

Other similar mixes may include homeopathic arnica (which is similar in its effect to Bach Flower Rescue Remedy), and often equisetum as well as comfrey to help with the restoration of normal bone tissue if structural changes have occurred in the bones themselves. Do not attempt to mix these up yourself because there are some cautions with some of the ingredients: devil's claw, comfrey and guaiacum, for example. However, mixed professionally and in the proper proportions, you have a safe, healing, anti-inflammatory treatment that will support your horse's healing, while making him more comfortable, and may even allow you to continue to work him in competition safely.

This sort of approach should always be the first choice for preventative treatment, management and first aid. Bute should be reserved for emergencies where pain and inflammation must be reduced as a matter of urgency under veterinary supervision and the risks associated with its use can therefore be justified. As with the herbs, the decisions as to treatment programs and dose levels in emergencies should be left to the professionals.

An herbal anti-inflammatory mixture, as stated, will need to be made up by a professional herbalist because of the cautions with some of the ingredients. These herbal mixes are usually in liquid form, and added to the horse's feed at 10 ml twice a day. For acute inflammation the dose is continued until the symptoms subside – usually in a few days to a week. Herbal anti-inflammatories also have the added benefit of being safe and side-effect-free for long-term use in chronic cases, such as the old horse with arthritis.

So, rather than having the usual box of bute sachets in the tack room in case of emergency (or, indeed, in case of slight discomfort, which often seems to be the case), consider having a bottle of an herbal anti-inflammatory made up and keep this on hand as a safe and very effective alternative.

Antibiotics

Recently, there has been a good deal of press coverage about the over-use and over-prescription of antibiotics and the subsequent emergence of resistant bacteria. It is not only in the area of human medicine that this is causing a problem, but also in the field of veterinary medicine where our animals suffer a similar fate.

The 'discovery' of antibiotics is considered the most important breakthrough in medicine in the twentieth century. This was of course another instance of the search for the active ingredient, whereby Alexander Fleming was actually seeking to find out what was the active ingredient in certain molds that were used by traditional healers to cure infection.

Beginning with the introduction of penicillin in the early 1940s, and the dramatic evidence of infection control in hospitals and during the Second World War, one disease after another fell to the constant onslaught of new and more powerful antibiotics. It was believed in those days that mankind could conquer, for all time, many of the infectious diseases that had plagued us for centuries.

After the war, research on these drugs quickly showed up the problem of 'drug resistance' and, as a result, for the first few years antibiotics were prescribed with caution. Bacteria, it turned out, were difficult to conquer. They are one of the oldest life forms on the earth and they have survived, and thrive, virtually everywhere precisely because they are adaptive, that is to say they are capable of changing themselves in response to a hostile environment. When bacteria are constantly exposed to antibiotics, they will do what they do best: adapt. If only a single bacterium manages to survive an antibiotic attack, that organism can produce over 16,000,000 offspring within twenty-four hours, and most of these will inherit the ability to resist that particular drug.

The post-Second World War era also saw the emergence of the modern multinational pharmaceutical companies and, quite quickly, they were falling over themselves to manufacture, promote and distribute antibiotics worldwide. What followed during the next forty years can only be seen as the irresponsible over-prescription and exploitation of these marvelous drugs by both the medical/veterinary profession and the multinational drug companies.

By the 1970s, most general practitioners routinely prescribed antibiotics, even for viral infections (just in case they develop into a bacterial infection); they were included in stock feed programs (not only for disease control but because they improved weight gain); and they were being pumped into hospitals at alarming rates.

It was during the same era that the first MDR (Multi Drug Resistant), strains of bacteria started to appear in hospitals. The most commonly known of these is 'Golden Staph' (*Staphylococcus aureus*), which was the first of the new 'superbugs' arising from medicine's ill-considered actions. In recent years Golden Staph, which can be fatal, has adapted to resist multiple antibiotics and infects patients through catheters, intravenous (IV) lines and wounds following surgical procedures. In the United States Golden Staph is the chief cause of infections in hospitals, contributing in up to 80,000 deaths annually.

Our faith in modern science was so strong that we believed the drug companies when they said we should not worry, that they would be able to come up with new drugs faster than bacterium became resistant to them. Of course this was to prove untrue. All the scientists knew it; government agencies knew it; hospital administrators knew it; and the medical profession knew it. However, it suited all these agencies to ignore the emerging problem because the profits being made from drug sales were so considerable that they certainly were not going to risk killing the goose that was laying the golden eggs.

As a result of professional, corporate and government irresponsibility then, we are now living in the dawn of the post-antibiotic era. Antibiotics, properly and responsibly used, could have served mankind for a thousand years. Instead, in a mere fifty years, we have abused and wasted them to the extent that hospitals are extremely dangerous places to go to; viruses and bacteria are crossing species lines (e.g. the Hendra virus – see Chapter 10: Exotic 'Bugs'); and we are facing a public health disaster of plague proportions with the return of new improved versions of the old killer diseases. Still we are not being told of the extent of the problem. There are hospitals that are being closed and burnt down around the world because they have lost control of resistant infections.

We are also not being told that there are alternatives. There are numerous ways, known by mankind since the dawn of time, of improving our own and our animals' immunity to infection. Garlic can cure pneumonia and typhoid, and has been regularly used by herbalists and as a folk remedy for this purpose since Mesopotamian times – only falling out of common usage in western societies with the advent of antibiotics. Preparations of silver (colloidal silver) were used throughout the Middle Ages and proved to be a natural broad-spectrum antibiotic. In fact, while most antibiotic drugs are effective against a select few types of bacteria, colloidal silver has been shown to kill over 650 different types of disease-causing bacteria and many viruses as well. Colloidal silver is also non-toxic and does not produce resistant strains of bacteria.

The body cannot utilize metallic silver and it must be converted to the colloidal state in order to be absorbed. Colloidal silver is an alchemic preparation of metallic silver, consisting of a suspension of minute particles of the metal (each particle consisting of twelve to fifteen atoms) prepared in plain water. In this state, silver can be easily absorbed and utilized by the body to fight bacterial and viral infections (here we have the origin of the expression 'born with a silver spoon in his mouth', which reflected the somewhat lower infant mortality experienced by the upper classes). Modern research shows that these colloidal particles seem to interfere with the respiration of the pathogens, which are thus unable to survive contact with colloidal silver. Indeed, some scientists believe that silver is necessary for the proper functioning of the normal immune system.

Before 1938, colloidal silver was manufactured by mechanical methods producing a very poor quality colloid. Nowadays we can produce it using a simple electrolytic process where very affordable equipment and materials can produce an almost endless supply of 5-10 ppm (parts per million) colloidal silver suspension in pure water. We are therefore in a position to manufacture our own antibiotics at home and in our hospitals. These compounds can also be used to sterilize our homes, stables and our hospitals when used as a spray.

Colloidal silver has proved to be very effective in the treatment of acute infections, as well as more long-standing, deeper-seated infections, and is a particularly good option for horse owners. However, do not inject colloidal silver in any circumstances: it should always be given orally or applied topically. A maintenance dose can be administered regularly to horses without fear of the horse building up a resistance, with a larger dose given in the case of specific infections. It can be administered orally to the horse and applied topically to wound sites and injuries to combat a wide range of bacteria. It is also cheap and far easier to administer than courses of injectable antibiotics, especially considering that the mere act of injecting a substance into a horse constitutes a trauma to his metabolism (see Vaccinations and Injections on page 99).

Combined with the specific herbal and homeopathic treatments, colloidal silver will be of enormous assistance to horse owners in making their charges 'bullet-proof' healthwise, in an era when we are bound to see more and more insidious diseases that cannot be treated by conventional veterinary science.

It is not hard to see why the multinationals are not interested in telling us about this material. It is harder to see why medical scientific institutions and bureaucracies are not interested. As usual it is left to the alternative medical field to keep the flame burning until some orthodox institution makes a major announcement and claims a 'breakthrough', and this will not happen until they can figure out a way to make big bucks out of colloidal silver!

Colloidal silver is available at a very reasonable cost from most health-food stores and alternative medical practitioners. It is also possible to make your own colloidal silver if you purchase the appropriate equipment – which is also available from alternative-health retailers.

Antioxidants

Antioxidants have received publicity recently for their role in treating cancer and other debilitating disease and have also been widely and successfully used by athletes to maximize performance. Antioxidants work by 'mopping up' free radicals in the body. Free radicals are the by-products of metabolism and of our contact with our increasingly polluted environment, which can accelerate the aging process and, in the end, can lead to the breakdown of the body's immunity.

For our animals, antioxidants perform exactly the same role as for humans and are proving to be extremely useful in strengthening the immune system and aiding performance. In fact, commercial vitamin C and vitamin E have been used for many years by performance trainers. Over recent times, Pycnogenol (the patented name of pine bark extract) has been sold for human consumption by pyramid marketing companies and has had a great deal of success in treating a wide range of conditions. This product is far stronger than the more traditional antioxidants – vitamins A, C and E – and is sold at astronomically inflated prices, which means that in general it has not been an option for horse owners.

My research has shown that wonderful results for humans and performance animals, at a minute fraction of the cost, could be achieved by simply making an extract of the bark of the maritime pine tree (*Pinus pinaster*). This tree is very common – in fact it is the main plantation pine species in many parts of the world. Extract of the bark has been well researched in Europe since the early 1960s and it has proved to be a major health tonic that supports the treatment of many debilitating diseases, as well as acting as a powerful preventative. Pine bark extract has been found to be an antioxidant fifteen to twenty-five times more powerful than vitamin C or vitamin E, which makes it an extremely powerful 'booster' to the immune system.

Weightlifters and body builders now use pine bark extract, which allows them to train harder than they could previously because it protects their capillary system from the damage done to tiny blood-vessels under extreme exertion. Therefore they can train harder without over-training; exactly the same is true of competition animals. Pine bark extract is a wonderful strengthener of the immune system for every horse and a particularly useful additive to the diets of performance horses. Interestingly, horses tied up to maritime pines will munch happily away on the bark.

Pine bark extract in concentrated drop form can be added to horses' feeds (twenty drops a day). If you can get hold of some bark of the maritime pine, crush it and simply make a tea from the dried bark by first boiling it for ten minutes and then steeping it (following the instructions for Making Herbal Tea in Chapter 2).

Poultices

Historically, the practice of applying poultices to promote healing, or to reduce swelling and inflammation, was a common and effective treatment for humans and animals. These days, although most people know what a poultice is, very few actually use them, which is a shame because they are an extremely effective, non-invasive natural healing aid for treating injuries and infections, particularly useful for many equine ailments.

Poultices are all external treatments usually applied directly to the skin, although they can be applied over a cloth or paper barrier to protect the skin from damage. A properly managed poultice will produce positive effects and no excess pain or tissue damage.

The reasons for poulticing are as follows:

- To bring heat to an area as heat improves circulation and the mobility of fluids within the adjacent tissue. This can speed healing, minimize scarring, reduce muscular spasm or assist in drawing toxins together to be expelled from the body.
- To act as a drawing agent to suck or to assist the flow of debris or toxins through openings in the skin.
- To hold medications, such as various herbs, in contact with the skin to aid the healing processes taking place in the area of the poultice.

Comfrey, garlic and castor oil are examples of herbs used in this way. All poultices consist of a carrier (some sort of mash, mud or slurry) and healing substances, usually herbs, oils or chemical substances, mixed with the carrier or applied under it. The carriers can be applied hot (but never so hot as to burn or blister), warm or cold. Poultices are usually held in place by loose bandages or wrappings of some sort and are therefore often difficult to apply over bulky muscular areas of horses. They are, however, ideal for the lower legs, which is an area subject to many problems in competition horses.

In a well-formulated poultice the carrier also has beneficial properties in itself (e.g. honey). There are limitless varieties of carriers available for use and you can use your imagination in formulating your own.

The following are some useful and effective poultice mixes, which can be combined/varied to suit many different situations:

- For any ligament or bone injury, a cup of linseed meal (ground linseed) mixed with half a cup of linseed oil and half a cup of minced comfrey leaves is an excellent remedy (just put all the ingredients in the blender). This treatment is applied warm and is traditionally very effective for breaks, chips, splints and torn or bowed tendons – speeding up recovery by a factor of two or three times. Caution: **do**

not use this poultice over an open wound or broken skin.

- An effective drawing poultice for cleaning out wounds, boils or infected pockets can be made by mixing four dessertspoons of slippery elm powder mixed with one dessertspoon of castor oil. The poultice can be made quite small and attached with a wide plaster over clean hair and/or a bandage to most areas on the horse. (Rug him if he tries to pull the plaster off, and the poultice is on a part of the body covered by the rug.) Please note that if using castor oil, you must only use it when there is a puncture hole in the tissue to draw through. Castor oil applied to the eye will draw metal filings out of a puncture wound and will clear mastitis from the teats of a lactating mare if applied between one feed and the next (to be washed off before the foal feeds).

- Rosemary oil, wintergreen oil, mustard and cajeput oil are all heating agents, which improve circulation and the mobility of fluids to aid in healing and minimize scarring. A tablespoon of rosemary or wintergreen oil is simply added to half a cup of honey and applied to the affected area. Mustard and cajeput are quite capable of blistering as they heat by irritation and so should only be used sparingly (only a few drops of cajeput, or a quarter teaspoon of mustard) added to half a cup of honey. A heating poultice should produce no more than a little swelling, any more and it can be counter-productive. Certainly anything that causes blisters is often doing much more harm than good.

- If your horse suffers an injury, has surgery, or any other condition that may be open to infection, you can crush 5–6 cloves of fresh garlic and add to a quarter cup of castor oil to make a poultice. Garlic is a powerful and natural antibiotic; and castor oil's drawing properties make it a wonderful treatment for a wound and will minimize the likelihood of infection by tetanus bacteria.

- Some old remedies for laminitis include: a linseed-meal poultice; a poultice made from bran and sea salt (one cup of salt to five cups of dampened bran); or a poultice made from boiled, pulped white turnips (about four turnips a poultice), all applied to the horse's affected feet after the shoes have been removed. These should be kept damp.

- A poultice to assist in the treatment of greasy heel consists of half a cup of ground linseed meal made into a thick porridge with a little boiling water, to which is added a cup of finely chopped groundsel or St John's wort. This should be kept damp. You can also add a teaspoon of thuja extract to this.
- For sand cracks in hooves: have the horse's feet trimmed correctly, then pack the crack with salt and half a cup of pulped rosemary (steam the fresh herb and then pulp).
- Swollen legs can be treated with cold packs made from rosemary or kelp (a handful of herb brewed in water and then drained) and mixed with a quarter cup of vinegar to form a paste.
- Sores that will not heal and areas of developing proud flesh can be cleaned up with a pawpaw poultice. First, make sure the area is clean and spray with antiseptic/styptic (see Herbal First Aid on page 91). Then apply a poultice made from fresh (very ripe) pawpaw flesh, mashed up, smothered over the wound, loosely bandaged and changed twice a day until the sore has healed or the proud flesh has completely gone.
- Hair can be encouraged to grow over hairless or rubbed areas using one handful of poplar buds (ground) with a quarter cup of castor oil and a quarter cup of honey, applied to the affected area twice a day for two weeks.

In general, it is advisable to leave a poultice on for forty-eight hours, take the covering off, rinse and leave the area unpoulticed for twelve hours and then apply a fresh poultice. Continue this cycle until the condition shows improvement.

Note Some horses have very sensitive skins, so it is always a good idea to test any substance you intend to apply to the skin on a small test area (behind the forearm is a good place), leave for twenty-four hours and check for any reaction. Most herbs will not cause any problems but do check with cajeput and mustard before slathering them on a large area. If possible, test the horse for anything you think you might need to use in an emergency while he is in good health and file the information away for future reference.

Supplements and Common Sense

Most horse owners and trainers nowadays give vitamins and minerals to horses as part of their daily program. Since the discovery of vitamin C and its link with the disease scurvy, we are accustomed to being told by the media and by health authorities that our health will be improved if we take additional vitamin and mineral supplements to our normal diets.

We are told that it is because of the modern lifestyle – stress and the denaturing of our soils etc. – that our food supply is not as good as it was in the 'old days'. This is of course true to some extent and we should be doing much more about the quality of our food – it is also true of the foodstuffs we feed our horses. However, adding the huge volume of expensive supplements to our horse's diets recommended by the 'experts' is just pouring money away as a result of clever marketing hype.

The truth is that vitamin and mineral supplements became such a lucrative market in human nutrition that they were quickly taken up by the animal feed and veterinary supply industries. Some of these products are harmless, some are detrimental to health and most are simply a waste of money.

Let us look at some of the individual vitamins and minerals often recommended by the advertising and where in nature they are readily available.

Vitamin A is found in carrots and leafy green vegetables and is therefore much better fed as such, rather than as processed supplements.

Vitamin B is found in all grains, so the idea of giving vitamin B supplements to animals that already have grain in their diet is ridiculous. Vitamin B12 is a little harder to get and is best found in the herb comfrey, which can be offered **occasionally and in small quantities** (no more than one fresh leaf a day) and in these doses is a valuable supplement.

Bioflavonoids can be supplied by a little buckwheat; especially for healthy blood vessels.

Vitamin C is found in fresh greens in abundance and it is a sorry horse that has no access to fresh green pasture! If a horse is kept away from greens for a time, tea made from a few rosehips tea bags in boiling water and allowed to cool, will provide all the vitamin C and iron that are missing.

Choline is found in bitter vegetables and the leaves of dandelions. A few fresh leaves can be offered to a stabled horse from time to time – otherwise, let a few dandelions grow around the yard and the horse will choose them for himself.

Vitamin D is synthesized by the action of sunlight on skin and found in fish oils and is not generally needed as a supplement for grazing animals.

Vitamin E is found in fresh wheat germ, along with the whole range of B vitamins. A little fresh wheat germ for those horses not on grains is all that is required.

Calcium is found in leafy greens and molasses (along with sulfur).

Iron is found in wheat germ, green feed and molasses.

Silica is found in dried feed in abundance.

Trace elements are all found in kelp.

So, your 'supplement regimen' can be as simple and inexpensive as feeding grains, green feed, a little wheat germ, molasses, carrots and kelp. To this, it is advisable to add garlic as a protection against infection and access to the odd weed like dandelion and comfrey.

Natural Tonics

As a daily health-giving feeding program, there are other natural alternatives to chemical additives. These natural tonics are simply added to the daily feed and you will be surprised at how quickly horses learn to savor them.

Boil 2 liters of water in the tack room every day and add two tablespoons of **rosehip** granules (or whole rosehips crushed). When this has gone cold, pour the concentrated tea (including the dregs) into the water container in the stable, or use it to damp down your horse's feed. There is no better kidney tonic or source of vitamin C and iron than rosehips. Avoid over-use of electrolytes and especially avoid using diuretics or potassium supplements because these substances weaken the kidneys very quickly.

Feed one cup of **millet** a day, (freshly ground or whole and soaked). Millet is very high in silica and it is silica and not calcium that is usually lacking when bone weakness or immaturity is a problem.

Feed one cup of **linseed** (freshly ground – not whole unless you feed it cooked) a day. Linseed has an affinity with ligaments and restores elasticity.

Make a mixture by submerging 750 gm of **garlic** cloves into a 5 liter tub of molasses and give half a cup of the resultant mix daily to your horse, cloves and all. Garlic and molasses are both high in sulfur and garlic is a natural antibiotic. In conjunction with the rosehips, this will do wonders for your horse's immunity.

A tablespoon of **kelp** (an excellent source of trace elements) either ground or in liquid form every few days is enough. Often the recommended dose for seaweed products is many times higher than is required in order to increase the volume sold. It is not harmful to give these larger doses, just wasteful. Ideally, allow the horse to 'free graze' his kelp from a container in his stable or yard.

Feed half a cup of fresh **wheat germ** a couple of times a week as a source of E and B vitamins.

Be wary of any product that has already been ground or cooked because the nutritional value of all seeds begins to deteriorate very quickly after grinding. Horses' metabolisms were not designed for cooked food (the exception being whole linseed).

Herbal First Aid

Herbs and Trauma

Because of their reactive natures as flight animals and the confined conditions in which we keep them, horses are inclined to injure themselves. This applies to the times when they are at liberty in the pasture, when being ridden and, particularly, when they are being transported (See Chapter 7: Herbs and Travel). Swift and appropriate first aid can go a long way towards minimizing the severity and long-term effects of any trauma or accident and herbal medicine provides horse owners with the means.

Shock

One of the major considerations in treating a horse for trauma – and especially after dealing with any life-threatening circumstance – is to deal with shock. Orthodox medicine has no specific treatment for shock whatsoever, which is amazing considering shock plays such a major role in health and the effects of trauma. Shock can dramatically alter the outcome of surgery; shock can exacerbate the complications following any injury by savagely depleting the immune system and adrenal reserves; shock also often produces nervous-system complications and reactions that remain in the system forever after a traumatic incident.

For this reason, the Bach Flower Rescue Remedy is an absolute must for the first-aid box, because it works by settling down and resolving the various energy components of shock: fear, panic, the heart-stopping jolt of trauma, vulnerability and loss of control. A few drops of Bach Flower Rescue Remedy administered to both horse and owner immediately after trauma dramatically improves the outcome by helping the owner make better decisions and to transmit calmer energy to the animal. It also effectively caps and unwinds the energy of shock spiraling out of control in the horse.

In a serious case, following the first dose the remedy needs to be given again after a short interval and then several more times that day and for the few days following. (Homeopathic arnica 30c works to relieve the physical repercussions of shock in a similar manner, but the Bach

Flower Rescue Remedy more fully covers the emotional ramifications of trauma in addition to the physical.)

Antiseptic/styptic

The next major component of a first-aid kit is an antiseptic/styptic mix to treat and sterilize open wounds. The best mix for these purposes contains twenty drops of stock strength (undiluted) Bach Flower Rescue Remedy and two other herbs: 100 ml each of extracts of yarrow and calendula. Yarrow is a styptic herb, which acts to seal small blood-vessels and reduce the bleeding while at the same time providing an energy boost to the physical nervous system. Calendula is an excellent general-purpose antiseptic, which will allow the body to gently control and expel any potentially infective agents. The mixture can be kept on hand at all times in a bottle or spray container.

The effect of using this sort of treatment as first aid for wounds is to reduce shock, seal small blood vessels and allow the wound to pull itself together from 'the inside out'. This is nature's way which, in the twentieth century, was supplanted by stitching the lip of the wound and pulling it together while possibly sealing in matter the body has not had time to expel. In this age of 'superbugs' in the environment, (especially in medical institutions!) and the failure of antibiotic therapy, it is vitally important to treat all wounds naturally as far as possible to avoid complications.

Apply a squirt of antiseptic/styptic immediately a wound is found then, as soon as possible, wash the wound out well and pat dry. Follow this with another generous squirt with the mixture. The wound can then be taped to hold it together and dressed to keep dirt out. Stitching will obviously still be necessary for large wounds but immediate and then continued use of the antiseptic/styptic mix as well will expedite healing. Change wound dressings regularly, applying more antiseptic/styptic each time and watch the wound granulate and heal from the inside out leaving the area almost completely scar free.

The Herbal First-aid Kit

All horse people have a first-aid kit in the tack room and there are some herbal and natural preparations that they should always have on hand.

The following table lists the items you should keep in the stable and their uses.

ITEM	USE
Herbal Liquid Preparations	
Bach Flower Rescue Remedy drops	For use in any trauma – for horse and human.
Antiseptic/styptic (see page 92)	Any open wounds as a first-line treatment and as a follow up in the healing process.
Anti-inflammatory (see page 76)	For any condition or wound involving the pain of inflammation.
Eyewash (see Chapter 10: Eye Conditions)	Foreign objects in the eye; any eye inflammation, irritation or infection.
Aloe vera gel	First-aid for sealing a burn wound (brands and rope-burns particularly).
Colloidal silver (see pages 81–83)	Topical and oral antibiotic/antiviral.
Chest and immunity mix (see Chapter 10: Respiratory System)	Herbal preparation for respiratory infection.
Travel trauma mix (see Chapter 7: Herbs and Traveling)	Before travelling, during a long trip and in case of any trauma.

ITEM	USE
Herbal Ointment Preparations	
Arnica	First aid for bruising and any physical trauma not involving broken skin.
Comfrey	To stimulate bone repair following injury and to minimize superficial scarring.
Calendula	Herbal antiseptic for use on broken skin.
Oils	
Castor oil	First-aid drawing agent.
Lavender oil	First-aid calming agent to assist in shock recovery, also a powerful antiseptic.
Eucalyptus oil	Topical antiseptic, sterilizes and in vapor-form an excellent inhalant.
Linseed oil	Used in poultices and for ligament health.
Hoof oil	A combination in a base of linseed oil containing wintergreen, white willow, arnica, comfrey and Bach Flower Rescue Remedy

ITEM	USE
Herbal Teas	
Chamomile tea	Parasympathetic nervous-system relaxant. Helpful as a colic prevention and in digestive and skin reactivity problems.
Rosehips tea	Iron and vitamin C tonic. Antioxidant, kidney, adrenal, liver and circulation tonic.
Fennel seeds	Pancreatic regulator, digestive tonic.

If traveling, the following should accompany you and your horse in case of emergency:

- Bach Flower Rescue Remedy
- antiseptic/styptic
- herbal anti-inflammatory
- travel mix
- eyewash
- Epsom salts, hydrogen peroxide
- towels, bandages, veterinary tape
- penknife, spare halter, shoe removing tools, syringes.

Natural Trauma Treatment

In the case of a trauma or accident to a performance horse, the conventional response is often to treat the horse with a range of pharmaceuticals and sometimes surgery and then, if that approach fails, rest is prescribed. Perhaps there might be a case for reversing the procedure.

Our bodies and those of our horses were designed to heal themselves; nature has provided all living creatures with healing mechanisms to help us recover from accident or trauma, along with instincts and an immune system to help us deal with illness. The fact is we often do more damage than good in our impatient efforts to intervene and treat as a first response.

In a natural environment there is absolutely no question that the best approach for all but a tiny number of accidents is first aid, followed by rest and a managed treatment and recovery program.

An Example: An Open Wound

By way of illustration, let us take the example of a horse that has gone through a fence sustaining a large open wound on the leg down towards the hoof and presenting with inflammation and pain in the leg and the hoof.

The orthodox approach

The orthodox approach may call for topical and intravenous antibiotics (to protect against infection), maybe probing to help clean the wound, sedation and stitching to attempt to close the wound, followed by bute for the pain and inflammation. Management advice may include stabling (to prevent the horse inflicting further damage) for some weeks, followed by some more weeks in a small stable yard (while the wound heals) and ongoing bute to manage the pain and inflammation while the leg heals.

The natural approach

The following is the more natural approach.

Immediately treat the horse for shock by giving Bach Flower Rescue Remedy orally.

If the injury involves arterial bleeding, call the vet immediately after attempts to stem the blood flow are in place because this condition demands immediate attention. If the blood flow is not arterial, call the vet as soon as you have the animal treated for shock and settled comfortably. The task of the vet is to evaluate, with minimal further stress to the animal, the pain levels involved and the extent of the injury in general terms.

After examination and evaluation, flush the wound with water and then apply an antiseptic/styptic combination of the herbs calendula and yarrow, to which has been added further Bach Flower Rescue Remedy. The styptic will seal blood vessels and encourage healing from the inside of the wound outward and the antiseptic will prevent infection. If the positioning and the nature of the wound allow the edges to be held together with tape or light bandages, do this. If this is not the case, do not worry about closing the wound, just attempt to organize a way in which it can be protected from further dirt or debris.

Bring the horse to comfortable protected surroundings and provide plenty of bedding and warmth as required for comfort. Continue to treat with Bach Flower Rescue Remedy and small repeated drenches of herbal teas made from dried rosehips and fresh hawthorn leaves, if available, for central nervous-system and adrenal shock.

For initial severe pain only, consider bute for one or two doses, administered by the vet as s/he sees fit. Rather, if debilitating pain persists, use herbal anti-inflammatories containing herbs such as white willow bark, which will reduce but not mask pain, allowing the horse to judge correctly what degree of movement is safe at the early stages of the healing process.

Ask your vet to come for a follow-up visit after two or three days to re-evaluate the extent of the injury and to decide if further intervention or surgery is absolutely necessary. During this visit it should also become clear if the horse's natural immunity is coping with any infection and, if not, the appropriate treatment should be discussed, maybe with input from your herbalist.

As soon as the horse's appetite returns, feed healing herbs suitable for supporting healing of injury and circulation to the area and to the hoof (see Chapter 10: Hoof Conditions). Continue to change dressings and to bathe the wound periodically, using simple antiseptic treatments like calendula or hydrogen peroxide. Arnica may be used to promote the reduction of soft tissue bruising and of bone bruising but should not be used until bleeding has stopped and not too close to the open wound. Topical herbal preparations should be applied regularly to the hoof to reduce inflammation and to promote circulation to the limb generally and healing within the hoof itself (see Chapter 10: Founder, for hoof-oil recipe).

As soon as the wound has sealed, preparations containing the herbs comfrey and linseed should be applied daily to support healing and to minimize scarring. These can either be in the form of poultices using the fresh leaf or root crushed into linseed oil and held in place with bandages, or the same ingredients mixed into an ointment base for those areas not amenable to strapping.

Allow the horse free access to an exercise yard and pasture, obviously managing distractions like other horses in the same enclosed area, but not locking him completely away from his companions.

Treat any signs of infection with natural antibiotic substances like garlic or colloidal silver, along with alterative herbs (see materia medica) to assist the immune system and the blood to deal with such problems. In fact, in the injury described in our example and treated as recommended, septicemia is extremely unlikely and could only occur if very obvious early signs were ignored.

Very quickly reduce all dependence on pain management - herbal or otherwise – and allow the horse free access to pasture and, ideally, to herbs. Freedom to exercise will speed the healing process. Walking and exercise will also allow the natural pumping action of the pedal bone to bring circulation to the hoof and leg and to carry fluids away via the same mechanism. Confinement can subvert this very important function, at best compromising the rate of healing and at worst leading to permanent damage within the hoof.

In the case of a competition horse, a structured work program should be recommended as soon as healing has progressed to the point that normal walking and running around has returned without lameness. While healing processes are still active, it is important to structure work to further focus healing on those areas needing extra strength and fitness for the sport in question.

After three weeks or so, arrange a further visit from a vet, trainer and/or other experienced professional in your particular sport to advise on specific flexing, exercise and appropriate training for this early stage of recovery and to lay out a program for the coming weeks. Herbal support is to be continued throughout this build-up in work. The herbal treatments should continue all the way up to 100% effort in training and be continued for the first three months of competition to ensure the horse is fully recovered all the way up to the full demands of the sport.

A fit dressage horse performing well in competition

Arrange a final visit from your vet after three months to assess if the horse is ready to commence full preparation, leading to competition fitness within the next three-month period. At the end of six months, expect the horse in this example to be in full work, totally recovered, and also expect no signs of weakness and only minimal scarring.

Vaccinations and Injections

Since the invention of the vaccination process, we routinely and increasingly vaccinate ourselves, our children, our horses, our dogs, our cats, farm animals (the list goes on), against the myriad perceived threats to health. We also take blood samples and administer antibiotics, anti-inflammatories, vitamins, sedatives etc. via a syringe. Horses suffer more from this reliance on the needle than do any of our other domestic animals.

A little-known, or rarely considered, fact is that every time we stick a needle (excluding acupuncture needles) into ourselves or an animal, we administer a grave shock to the immune system. The scenario is this: the immune system is quietly motoring along, doing its thing when, suddenly, a foreign substance is injected, bypassing the normal channels, straight into the bloodstream, sending the whole immune system immediately into shock.

The body of a human or animal is designed to take in substances through the mouth and the digestive tract, through inhaling and through the skin – all of these processes are slow and natural and allow the immune system time and warning. The application of a needle into vein or muscle is instantaneous and invasive and always results in shock. The shock effect is the same whether the substance is administered as a stimulant, a medicine, the best vitamins man can manufacture, pure saline or even your own blood as in 'blood doping' in human athletes.

These shocks accumulate and, along with the environmental and feeding changes we have inflicted on our equine friends in good faith, we have adversely affected their health and wellbeing.

Vein Damage

Unfortunately, it is not uncommon to see cases of damage to the jugular veins in horses, as a result of frequent and/or inappropriately administered intravenous injections. In such cases, it is possible to use herbs very successfully to assist in repairing the damage.

Make up a mix containing a cup each of the following herbs: millet, linseed, yarrow, nettle and rue in the dried herb form; comfrey and hawthorn in extract form (10 ml of each); and twenty drops of Bach Flower Rescue Remedy. This mixture is combined and fed in the quantity of a cup in the morning and a cup at night mixed well into the horse's feed. This formulation provides both the nutrients and the impetus for re-establishing a healthy vein wall, promotes the reabsorption of the scar tissue resulting from the injury and treats the horse for shock.

In addition, rub on a 5% witch hazel cream in a sorbolene base (available from health-food stores) as an external astringent tonic. This is applied once a day, in the morning, around the area of the vein itself to promote tone and elasticity in the local area. In the afternoon, apply the herbal hoof oil preparation (see Chapter 10: Founder, for the formulation) to the vein. This formula has anti-inflammatory actions, promotes local healing and provides stimulation to the horse's circulation.

The results of this program can be dramatic. Damage, which is often regarded as permanent, will usually resolve itself within six weeks of the treatment, sufficiently so as to be only noticeable under close examination, and the full restoration of blood flow through the vein should occur at the end of eight weeks treatment. Continue the treatment for another two weeks.

Precautions

It would be inappropriate and irresponsible to suggest that you should never inject your horse, sometimes it is unavoidable (in emergency situations etc.). However, there are ways you can avoid many of the 'injectables': avoid blood testing; give your horse his vitamins in natural form; nourish and support his nervous system as a replacement for sedatives; and give some thought to replacing some of your regular vaccinations (tetanus, strangles, influenza etc.) with homeopathic alternatives (see the References section for texts that deal with this in detail), or at the very least reducing the frequency of the booster shots and using alternatives to afford your horse protection between boosters.

There are also precautions you can take should an injection be unavoidable – and this is true for humans, horses, dogs, cats, etc. Have on hand half a lemon, some Bach Flower Rescue Remedy and some extract of thuja. Give the Bach Flower Rescue Remedy and the thuja to the patient immediately before and after the injection and, as soon as the injection has been given, place the cut side of a freshly cut lemon on the site. The Bach Flower Rescue Remedy and thuja will deal with the shock and reduce the possibility of introducing infection through the puncture wound. The lemon causes all the tissues around the needle site to contract, effectively slowing down the absorption process and giving the immune system more time to deal with the contents of the syringe. This strategy will give the immune system the best chance of coping with the invasion.

5 Herbs and the Performance Horse

Perfect Health

Like human athletes, our performance horses need to be in absolutely optimum health in order to reach their full potential. This applies to racehorses, pacers, dressage horses, endurance horses, eventers, showjumpers, cutting horses – any horse that is required to perform in an equine sport.

This would suggest that among performance horses we would find the fittest, healthiest and heartiest specimens of the species. Not so! In fact our current generation of performance horses are far more frail (and expensive to maintain) than their predecessors and at the same time they are expected to perform more frequently and at increasingly higher levels of exertion and activity. The attrition rate of performance horses around the world is horrendous.

Maintaining all horses in perfect health should be the horse owner's aim and this is even more crucial when it comes to performance horses. As we have already seen, using chemical foodstuffs, additives and pharmaceutical drugs is getting us exactly nowhere. The prerequisite for peak performance is perfect health and this can best be achieved naturally.

Perfect health is not the absence of symptoms of illness: "OK for my age I guess", "Don't take medicines much", "OK after I get going", "Pretty good after my morning coffee". These are all comments from patients, which reflect about 'five and a half out of ten' on the scale of wellbeing.

Perfect health is that feeling of boundless physical energy and enthusiasm for life: "Jumping out of my skin", "Energy to burn", "Skipping on the way to school", "Never get sick", "Can fight off a cold or flu in two or three days", "Hungry for my meals", "Sleep anywhere", "Bounce out of bed raring to go", "Never depressed", "Boundless enthusiasm", "Recharge my battery with a fifteen minute nap". These are all 'ten out of ten' comments. This state of health is our birthright; we were meant to feel like this all of our lives, as should our horses.

We all know the look of a horse in perfect health: shiny coat, bright eyes, running and bucking in the pasture out of sheer exuberance, keen, alert, ears forward, enjoying work, easy to manage, relaxed before competition, never off his feed, never depressed or requiring the vet. This state of health should be a prerequisite for all our competition horses and you cannot just hope that this will somehow happen on its own – although it sometimes seems to. We must raise, manage, train and nourish our horses so that this is how they feel every single day.

This is perfect health. This is what this book is all about and you should not accept less than this, either for yourself or for your horse. Now that *is* a challenge!

Herbal Performance Enhancement

Unfortunately, to the owner of an equine athlete, performance enhancement often means chemical intervention. In fact, the ultimate and really *only* true performance enhancement is by supporting the horse in reaching his full potential. For this he needs perfect health.

Really, a lot of the time, performance horses go well despite us rather than because of us. If you look at the huge variety of practices that exist in the fields of mating, rearing, handling, breaking, training, feeding and managing performance horses, you cannot help wondering if we really do know what we are doing.

Basically, besides trying to keep your performance horse in a manner that resembles his natural habitat and feeding good quality, natural foodstuffs, using herbs to maintain the performance horse in top condition is the best possible performance enhancer.

The Performance Tonic for Equine Athletes

The following herbal tonic supplies all that is required to encourage 110% performance out of a 100% fit and well performance horse. At the same time, this formulation improves the horse's ability to perform at his peak for much longer and to recuperate quickly.

What is interesting and informative is to examine the various ingredients in the mixture and to illustrate the philosophy of herbal medicine as applied to the task of getting the best out of a healthy equine athlete in the modern age.

The task at hand, then, is to produce a tonic that will:

- Enable the horse to perform in performance at the absolute top of his ability.
- Maximize the efficiency of the heart and the blood to supply oxygen to, and clear waste products from, the muscles.
- Maintain and conserve high levels of adrenalin in reserve.
- Maintain the nervous system at peak, but not wasteful, readiness prior to performance and keep the brain and intelligence engaged and focused on the job at hand.
- Support the metabolic and nervous systems so that the horse enjoys his work, will recuperate quickly and be keen for more.
- Support the horse's immunity and the physical systems to minimize 'down time' and maximize his 'working' life.

Bearing the above criteria in mind, the following are the herbal ingredients which, together, will support all these aims and enhance the performance of a top equine athlete. A full week's supply of tonic can be prepared by combining two cups of each of the following dried herbs:

Yarrow is a high organic iron source and a blood tonic, working especially to stimulate bone-marrow production of red blood cells. Yarrow also functions as a support to the nervous system under high physical stress loads.

Nettle is the highest common vegetable source of iron and maximizes the ability of the blood to carry the required levels of oxygen to the muscles and the heart.

Dandelion supports both the liver and the kidneys. These two organs are primarily responsible for cleaning the blood of both metabolic waste products and the waste products from high levels of exercise. Dandelion will help prevent 'tying up' and will repair some of the damage done by the routine use of electrolytes, diuretics and exotic chemical supplements so common in the equine industry. In harmony with rosehips and kelp, dandelion also assists the metabolism to return to normal quickly after performance, preventing the horse from falling away after competition.

Hops are a nervous-system tonic specifically suited to an overly busy head under stress. The effect of hops in the system is to allow the horse to be keyed up ready for competition but not to be so highly strung that he is competing before the start of the event.

Borage is a primary adrenal tonic used through the ages to bolster courage and performance under stress. As a relative of comfrey, it also has valuable healing properties to counter the physical wear and tear of exercise at peak performance.

Add one cup each of the following:

Rosemary is a circulation stimulant, especially to the muscles and to the brain, both of which must be working at peak in a competition situation.

Kelp provides all the trace elements that could be lacking in the horse's diet, along with providing direct support and stimulation to the thyroid and pituitary glands, which are fundamental to total health and performance.

Rosehips support the kidneys, the adrenals and the blood and are a major source of natural vitamin C and of organic iron compounds. Kidney health is critical to the health of adrenal glands and it is the adrenal glands that provide the extra drive needed to win on the day.

The rosehips should be made into a herbal tea by infusing about fourteen tablespoons of rosehip granules into 7 liters of boiling water which is allowed to go cold. To this infusion the following liquid extracts should be added at a rate of 20 ml each. (This infusion, which is sufficient to go with a full week's supply of tonic, is stored in a refrigerator or cool room or, in hot climates, made up in smaller quantities to avoid it going off.)

Maritime pine extract is a major antioxidant some twenty-five times more powerful than vitamin C, as well as a direct support for the peripheral circulatory system. Exposure to this herb minimizes damage to small blood vessels under heavy work and speeds up the absorption of free radicals produced under stress.

Hawthorn extract is a major heart tonic which will allow the heart to work at peak without stress or long-term strain. Again, hawthorn is one of those herbs that will allow an animal to draw upon very deeply hidden reserves in the final stretch.

Combine the dry ingredients well and feed one cup of the mix morning and night, mixed with feed. A $\frac{1}{2}$ liter of the liquid components should also be mixed through each feed. This tonic can be fed daily while the horse is engaging in competition.

In general terms, the above formulation will assist most healthy equine athletes to perform at their best week after week. The mix does not, however, address specific weaknesses, which an individual animal may be prone to either structurally or metabolically. Other horses have the need for individual nervous-system support so sometimes the ingredients will need to change to address these individual requirements. In these cases, seek the services of a professional herbalist to customize your performance herbal blend.

Horses are purpose-bred for the various equestrian and sporting disciplines – each area having its own specific requirements and needs – and judicious use of herbs and natural horsekeeping practices can maximize the chance of success. While all the above information applies to any equine performance horse, there is some specific information that applies to some of the different sporting areas, which follows below.

Racers and Pacers

Herbal 'cures' and secret recipes to make horses go faster (or slower) have been around forever and there is a large amount of folklore about such things. As a result of the 'backlash' against chemical preparations that are failing to work and simultaneously causing health problems in our horses – combined with the increasing rigorousness of drug testing in most racing sports – racehorse trainers and owners are rapidly coming to realize the benefits of herbal preparations.

Nerves

The most successful breeders and trainers, however, do have one thing in common: they know that the champion performance horse is the relaxed performance horse and they go to great lengths to train their animals with this always in their minds. Having treated large numbers of racing and pacing horses for many years now, it is clear that the most common reason for the failure of a talented horse to deliver his potential is that he leaves his energy behind at the starting gates. It is not just that he is nervous on race day, it is that the combination of all his experiences and handling up to the racetrack have caused the horse to squander his adrenal reserves before the start. Basically, there is nothing left 'in the tank' for when it is needed, especially on the home stretch.

This is where herbs can be of immense value in balancing and nourishing the horse's nervous system so that energy is conserved for the race. The best approach to preparation is the holistic one, in which all aspects of health, training, feeding and wellbeing should be considered to produce the best product.

Often a pattern of behavioral and nervous problems starts as soon as the foal receives his first trauma or shock. This could be something as apparently insignificant as the mare being treated with antibiotics for infection while in foal or while feeding. Weaning can also be a time of considerable trauma for the foal, depending on the level of management existing at the particular stud.

Without a doubt, yearling preparation, subsequent sale, breaking and pretraining is the time when the most damage is done to the young horse's nervous system.

There are several distinctly different nervous-system types found commonly in racehorses and support with appropriate herbal combinations, along with care in all that early handling and training, goes a long way towards ensuring an individual racehorse has a confident and relaxed outlook on life.

Certain types of nervous reactions will tell you which herb a horse needs to nourish his nervous system. A horse that needs chamomile often tends to be a 'gut reactor' and produces frequent loose manure (or even suffers from colic) at times of stress; the vervain type is the one that appears permanently agitated, distracted and fidgety, has superacuity of all five senses and is easily startled and often particularly skin reactive – sweating at times of stress and breaking out with skin irritations; the valerian type is characterized by holding himself far too tightly in the muscular sense, thereby depleting the oxygen supply to the muscles (see Chapter 4: Nerve Tonics).

A correct assessment of the basic nervous-system type is what the top breeders do instinctively when matching blood lines to produce an animal that is relaxed while, at the same time, on his toes, alert, keen and confident. Nourishing and strengthening a horse's nervous system from the very beginning by appropriate handling and herbal supplements gives a major competitive advantage in the quest for a champion.

Fear and confidence are the two big problems the young racehorse has to contend with: fear of going to the barrier; reluctance to jump out; preference for hanging back in the field; tendency to bolt to the front; fear of being held in the mob in the middle of the field – the list is endless.

The area of fear, panic, distraction, apprehension, lack of confidence, or perhaps too much energy and misplaced confidence, is one that can very easily be remedied using a variety of homeopathic treatments, either alone or in conjunction with nervous-system herbs. Most importantly, using these sorts of remedies can also treat the continuing after-effects of an accumulation of shock and trauma (see Chapter 9: Bach Flowers and Other Alternative Therapies).

Herbal support and conventional treatments
Beyond nervous-system considerations for the racehorse, herbal support for adrenal and kidney function; circulation and the heart; ligament and

bone strength and elasticity; and digestion and absorption, will produce a horse with 'bullet-proof' health and wellbeing.

The best approach is to use herbs in the young horse's preparation as above and as preventative medicine, to balance and nourish all the systems in the horse to prevent problems developing. Respiratory problems, like infections resulting from a weakened immune system, or from bleeding resulting from weakened blood-vessel walls in the lungs, along with structural problems in the ligaments, bones, joints and hooves, are the main areas of concern for the racehorse in work.

All of these areas are best considered preventatively in supplement programs and best treated using non-invasive herbal treatments as the first line of attack. Save up the 'big guns' of chemical medicines, injections, operations, scopes, blood tests, scans, X-rays, etc. for real emergencies and minimize the horse's exposure to shock, trauma, chemical poisoning, reactions etc. There is certainly a place for modern medicine and medical technology but it should be used in conjunction with natural treatments if required, rather than as the first line of treatment. All herbs are best used ahead of any sort of chemical treatment that is aimed at eliminating symptoms while ignoring the underlying causes of ill health.

Problems of wear and tear leading to the early onset of arthritis and rheumatism patterns can be largely averted by a sensible approach to feeding management, training and the use of preventative herbal treatments. However, when they do occur there are many tried and true herbs to speed and complete the healing process. Some of these are: arnica, celery, comfrey, equisetum, linseed, millet, silica and yarrow (see Chapter 10: Arthritis and Rheumatism).

There is a large range of herbs which is valuable in treating inflammatory processes and is preferable to the use of bute with its dangers and side-effects. These include: arnica, devil's claw, guaiacum, white willow and wintergreen (see Chapter 4: Anti-inflammatories).

Blood-cleansing herbs or alteratives include: dandelion, echinacea, garlic, nettle, red clover and rosehips. There are kidney herbs, heart herbs, lung herbs, herbs to promote circulation, herbs to increase blood supply to the brain or to the lower limbs, herbs to support digestion etc. – dozens and dozens of them. See the materia medica at the end of the book for the simplest and most practical ones covered in this text, and Chapter 10, which deals with specific conditions. For a general tonic, see The Performance Tonic for Equine Athletes on page 104.

Tendon management

With performance horses – racehorses in particular - tendon problems are widespread and often signal the demise of a promising athletic career. Understanding how they work is the first step in avoiding and dealing with tendon damage. Research shows us that tendons are designed with a crimp running along the length of their fibers. This is the first stage of elasticity that acts like a shock absorber to soften the build-up of tension on a tendon at the beginning of a load situation - rather like taking up the slack before coming under load. This crimping decreases with age and is lost in any area of tendon that has been over-stretched and then healed.

In full work, the tendons of a racehorse are working at very near to their design limits, which means there is almost no safety margin left in the tendon at full stretch. Tendons have been tested and shown to begin to fail at around 15% stretch in the laboratory. Tests on racehorses in full work show that tendons are subjected to stretch very close indeed to these absolute limits. Tendons heat up during work and blood vessels involved in the blood flow within them rupture when the tendons begin to fail, thus causing the tendon to swell and to bow.

The horse's body has two stages of healing when repairing damage to tendons. The first 'emergency' stage is to rapidly grow links between the individual strands of damaged tendon fibers to give emergency support, almost immediately, to the area after injury. Over time, this cross-linking reduces as the repair work on the longitudinal fibers proceeds during the second stage, which begins around thirty days after the original injury. However, this cross-linking never reduces to its original level and many months are involved until it is minimized.

Conclusions we can draw from this research are as follows:

- In gallopers especially, the damage to, and the resulting 'ageing' of, tendons begins at a very young age and as soon as they are put under racing workloads. This is exacerbated by the fact that they are put into work before their ligaments and bones have fully matured, which might not, in nature, be completed until around five years of age.

- That anything which can speed the maturity and improve the elasticity and strength of tendons to give even tiny extra margins of safety could have very significant impact on the whole pattern of damage and ageing and therefore the whole career of the horse.
- That much more attention should be paid to pretraining to encourage and stimulate maximum strength and elasticity in the tendons, with the long-term viability firmly in mind rather than just the two-year-old stakes.
- That a warm-up and cool-down before and after work is critical and that anyone who is cutting corners in this regard is criminally compromising the long-term viability of the horse.
- That there are opportunities to assist in the healing of minute strain injuries, which are occurring almost routinely during work and training and that science has not really gone beyond hosing the legs and the ice pack in this regard.

Along with following the natural management suggestions listed throughout the book, there are a few strategies for high-level performance-horse owners to follow that can help to minimize the potential for tendon damage.

Prewarm-up strategy
Use a cream with extracts of arnica, rosemary, maritime pine and wintergreen (have your herbalist make this up for you – cautionary measures are necessary with arnica and wintergreen) and lightly massage it into the horse's legs before warm-up for all training and racing sessions.

Neoprene-type boots should be left off during warm-up and heavy work and replaced, if necessary for support or for protection, with a material that can breathe and facilitate cooling. It seems logical that using such insulating, non-porous materials as neoprene must severely reduce heat dissipation from connective tissue under work. The build-up of heat and the reduction of internal blood supply within the tendon while in heavy work compromises cooling, so why risk further reduction in cooling by insulating the leg? Instead, use porous bandages, if required for support, and pads to prevent knocking particular areas but nothing to trap heat. Any interference with cooling must push the tendons closer to their limits and make them more prone to injury or failure.

The choice of herbs for this situation is mostly built around the premise that if we can maximize the circulation and thereby the cooling within the tendon and surrounding tissues, while at the same time supplying healing herbs topically and internally on a routine basis during maturation and training, we can easily improve the safety margin between the design limits and demand load. Any tiny improvement will substantially reduce the damage and the cumulative 'ageing' of tendons occurring during every training and racing session.

Postwork strategy

The use of a concentrated herbal-extract mix after work would also be of enormous benefit. The herbs involved in this mixture are arnica and maritime pine, along with comfrey and equisetum. These herbs aim to speed up and normalize all the minute and quite normal incidents of wear and tear occurring during training and athletic performance and provide direct and immediate support to healing within both the bones and the connective tissues.

This extract is mixed into water and sprayed on the horse's legs after a proper cool-down followed by hosing down as the legs are beginning to dry. These herbs will be carried down the hairs to the skin and form a healing residue that will last at least until the next work session or until the legs are hosed down again when – for a racehorse in full work – the spray should be reapplied.

Internal Treatments

As part of the racehorse's lifetime feeding regime, use a supplement consisting of millet, linseed, comfrey, equisetum and yarrow. This will continually supply the extra nutrients required to speed maturity and development and provide internal support for all healing processes during work, strain and injury.

The unacceptably high state of attrition in the racehorse industry is well recognized and for those trainers and owners who are interested in protecting their considerable investment in bloodstock, herbal medicine as a preventative as well as a primary treatment is an attractive and intelligent option.

Recycling Racehorses

Many horses are 'recycled' from the racetrack to become eventers, showjumpers, dressage horses, hacks or just pleasure horses. Careful selection of the right horse can make this a very successful and rewarding exercise for the horse owner, whilst rescuing a horse from the 'equine scrap heap'. However, a horse that has been subjected to the rigors of racing will usually have specific problems (both physical and psychological) that will need to be dealt with before he can start his new life and herbal treatments have a lot to offer in this area.

Resting

When you first take your new horse home, you should give him a break for at least twelve weeks to allow a transitional period. This is of great psychological benefit for the horse and gives you a chance to use herbs and common sense to get his nervous system and metabolism back on track. During this break, the horse should have free access to grass and preferably also weeds, as part of his diet. It is a good idea to take his shoes off as well during this time and, if possible, he should have access to other horses to learn how to be a horse again.

This period is the best time to start with herbal tonics and medicines to treat pre-existing injury or weaknesses. It is also a good time to introduce your horse to the addition of garlic, molasses and kelp to his diet (see Chapter 4: Natural Tonics). There are a variety of herbal and natural products that support the restoration of physical soundness (especially tendon, bone and hoof problems – see Chapter 10) and the restoration of the nervous system (see Chapter 4: Nerve Tonics).

These are simple and inexpensive treatments that will ensure that you use the resting and retraining time to best advantage. Even quite long-standing and severe physical problems – such as bowed tendons, shin soreness, splints and hoof problems – can be made fully sound in a fraction of the time you would expect (see Chapter 10: Bones and Connective Tissues).

Respiratory problems such as bleeding, roaring, allergy or low resistance to chest infections can also easily be corrected during the normal resting and retraining phase, if the correct herbal and training treatments are prescribed (see Chapter 10: Respiratory System) .

Retraining

After his break, you will already be well on the way to dealing with any physical problems and supporting your new horse's metabolism with herbs and the chance to simply behave like a horse. Now it is time to consider beginning his re-education in preparation for his new career.

The retraining program you choose will be the one that suits you but take care to nurture the horse's nervous system and to follow a regimen based on mutual respect rather than fear or dominance if your aim is to have a willing partner. During the resting period, you will have begun his physical and psychological rehabilitation but when you actually begin to work with your new horse, this is when his temperament, 'horseonality' and nervous 'type' will become really apparent. This is the time to refine and really use the herbs you identify as his nerve tonics (see Chapter 4: Nerve Tonics). Passion flower is almost always recommended for the recycled racehorse in addition to his identified nervine/s as it acts as a catalyst in changing ingrained behavior. Bach Flower Remedies are also invaluable at this time to help the horse's emotional state (see Chapter 9: Bach Flowers).

What you are aiming for is to arrive in the competition ring with a horse fully sound in mind and body and looking forward to working with you in your chosen sport. The right environment, training and feeding, combined with the judicious use of herbs, will give you the best possible chance of achieving your end.

Equine Athletes

Equine athletes that are not used solely for the racetrack also have special needs, whether they are showjumpers, eventers, cutters, reiners, barrel racers, or dressage horses. They are subjected to similar stresses to the racehorse and, in the case of showjumpers or eventers, are often recycled from the racetrack into a showjumping or eventing career.

Often, also, horses are purpose-bred for their specific careers. True performance enhancement begins at birth, so to deal with the rigors of their careers, young horses need to be cared for really carefully during their developmental stages. Early attention to the development of bones and ligaments and fanatical attention to injuries or lamenesses as the horse is growing will pay off later as he grows into a strong equine athlete.

The usual warnings also apply: do not start the horses too young; keep the work varied and interesting; do not keep them locked up in small areas; develop a management program that aims to keep a horse for 'the long haul', not as a 'throwaway' item. Care for their mental as well as physical wellbeing: do not employ barbaric training practices such as 'rapping', and adopt a feeding and care regimen that is as natural as possible.

Put all young horses on millet, linseed (see Chapter 4: Natural Tonics), yarrow and comfrey (see Chapter 2: Making Herbal Teas) to bring them up from weaning and treat the slightest injury, lameness or soreness in their limbs with arnica, comfrey and linseed externally (see Chapter 10: Bones and Ligament Problems). This simple but specific program during their first couple of years will create young equine athletes with physically superior maturity, strength and elasticity that will last them for the rest of their careers. Also, incorporate the usual herbal support for the immune system and all other metabolic processes mentioned in the other sections of the book.

For herbal support during competition, see the suggestions in the section on Electrolytes (Chapter 4) and the following section on herbs for the endurance horse.

Endurance Horses

Endurance riders, by necessity, are knowledgeable about their horses and their needs for the often grueling sport they undertake and they know better than any other horse people do *exactly* how their horses react to heavy workloads. They are also very often quite low budget sports people given to sensible and simple common-sense solutions to problems.

Herbs and natural feeding and medication practices have helped a great number of people competing in endurance and the results have been seen by the riders in dramatically improved readings at every vetting station along the ride. Herbs that are particularly helpful for horses competing in endurance rides (and eventers) are the following (see Chapter 2: Preparing Herbs, for details on administering the herbs).

Borage aids in the management of adrenal energy. Borage is particularly suited to the big-hearted tryer and so many successful endurance horses certainly qualify for this title. The secret to success in endurance is to start a ride with a full tank of adrenaline and to use it very sparingly along the ride; borage enables the horse to do just that.

Yarrow is an herb that is very high in iron and this assists the bone marrow in red blood cell production. Again, yarrow is the sort of herb well suited to boosting oxygen efficiency and distribution at the level of the red blood cells. Maximizing red blood cell health and vitality maximizes the oxygen-carrying capability of the horse's blood to the whole system.

Rosehips should be fed as an herbal tea, with both tea and the dregs fed to the horse routinely, but especially in the few days before a big ride. We also encourage the riders to carry and drink the tea cold on the race as well as giving it to their horses. Rosehips provide iron, vitamin C, adrenal support, kidney support and, as an antioxidant, also supports the immune system.

Maritime pine clears free radicals generated by athletic exertion at a phenomenal rate (see Chapter 4 – Antioxidants). It also protects the circulatory system and is immediately obvious in lessening stiffness and soreness after strenuous exercise.

Hawthorn leaves and berries are a major heart tonic, which is particularly valuable to speed heart-rate recovery.

Endurance horses and riders also benefit from several homeopathic ingredients like the **Bach Flower Remedies larch**, **oak** and **vine** (5-6 drops every hour or so during competition) to aid staying power and confidence.

Prevention of Injury

Equine athletes are more at risk of injury than pleasure horses because of the nature of the activities they undertake. The art of 'building' the ultimate performance horse starts with selecting the right bloodlines for the job, supporting the mare through the pregnancy and being fanatic about feeding, treating and maintaining the young horse. Basically, injury prevention begins with rearing and preparation and herbally there are wonderful opportunities to support and enhance the physical and emotional development of foals and young stock. This is dealt with in Chapter 6: The Youngster.

The most serious source of injury problems is the modern practice of breaking and training horses as two-year-olds. This is rather like heavy impact or weight training for a ten-year-old child athlete. The bones of most young horses have not matured sufficiently to cope with the work required to race, pace or cut cows as a two-year-old. This is only the visible part of it. Most young horses have also not matured sufficiently to cope emotionally with modern performance preparation programs either.

The practice of subjecting young horses (many of them no more than foals) to rigorous exercise before they are physically developed often leads to bone and tendon problems and shin soreness. The performance industry often deals with these problems in a frighteningly barbaric manner. Besides impatient and cruel breaking practices still being part of so much normal preparation, pin-firing is the most barbaric of the 'medical' techniques still used on young horses. Can you imagine, for example, how society and the legal system would deal with someone using this practice on children to prepare them for a career in marathon running? Suffice to say that allowing horses to develop naturally would make these barbaric practices unnecessary.

At least we still leave foals with their dams to be reared in the open and weaned naturally, unlike the experiences of many other animals raised by man, so horses at least have that period to develop as nature intended.

A balanced diet of natural feed, both fresh and dried, is essential, as is the absolute minimization (preferably 'almost total exclusion') of all processed feeds and supplements. Include millet and some linseed in the performance horse's diet to enhance bone and ligament health and maturity (see Chapter 4: Natural Tonics). Allow access to the hedgerow herbs listed in Chapter 3, especially yarrow, dandelion, comfrey, nettle and fennel. Provide, but do not force feed, natural supplements like rock salt, dolomite and kelp. Practice cross-training by introducing dressage or other disciplines into all performance horses' preparation.

More important even than feeding is the practice of foresight and care in the management of new and potentially traumatic experiences like medical procedures, vaccinations and trailering, along with all breaking and training. This is where Bach Flower Rescue Remedy and other trauma treatments and first-aid practices are so important (see Chapter 4 – Herbal First Aid).

Consistency of behavior and empathy in the carers and handlers, along with companionship and play with other young horses are also all very important aspects of injury prevention.

Protection from poor design of surroundings is also very important. Going through fences, going down in a trailer, or going down a hole in the field are all experiences that can end a performance horse's career before it starts.

The best advice for the prevention of injury is to observe, listen and learn how to improve your horse's total physical and emotional environment and never stop doing it. Do not rely on herbs, or professionals, or any other single aspect of horsekeeping to do the whole job. Do it holistically and do it yourself.

Rest and Recuperation

The role of resting in the case of any health or injury problem is well-documented, for humans and animals, and left to their own devices horses will use rest for healing. In a natural environment there is absolutely no question that a rest is the best first approach for all but a tiny number of illnesses or accidents: first aid and then rest. However, we like to intervene feeling that we can speed up the recuperative process.

This is particularly true for performance horses where 'down-time' is often seen as a waste of monetary resources. The argument used by professionals is that they should try the medical or surgical approach first to try to get horses back in action quickly. Of course, if the treatment is dealing only with symptoms, the underlying problem remains and probably gets worse. If antibiotics are used routinely, new and resistant bugs are encouraged and immunity and digestive efficiency are impaired. If surgery is only partially successful, the body may be left unable to ever effect a complete cure during resting.

What often happens after conventional veterinary treatment is that, far from having the horse back in work quickly, recovery is extremely slow or even impossible. Maybe in the long and even the short term, the most cost-effective approach to getting a performance horse back into work would have been to conduct a medically-supervised convalescence and recovery program as a first step for most cases of illness or injury.

A considered program of medical rest and recuperation, when horses are placed in an equestrian facility under supervision and given specific feed and exercise programs along with medicinal herbs, will effect a complete recovery from even the most severe problems in a short time. Herbal treatments are complete within themselves and require nothing more than a healthy and caring environment; a sensible and supportive feeding program; and a constructive exercise program in order to produce 'miraculous' recoveries.

The ideal medical rest and recuperation program would consist of co-operation between a knowledgeable herbalist and the owners of horse facilities who can offer the three factors above in support of the treatments.

The areas that could be covered in a medical R and R program would be: postoperative recovery; tendon, bone and hoof injuries; bleeding lungs and other respiratory problems; nervous-system complaints; and metabolic problems ('poor doers').

Using herbs and the above criteria, on average, resting times would be reduced by 60% or more. The owners (and perhaps vets and trainers) could be provided with progress reports, together with a discharge report making detailed suggestions of an on-going program of diet, supplements and support during training and competition. Under this system, the horses would be returned fit, healthy and ready for training at a cost far below that of conventional treatments.

Herbs and Legal Competition

A common question asked by horse owners from all sports and disciplines is, "Are herbal products legal for competition?" Herbs are naturally occurring plants, and a positive swab is highly, if not completely, unlikely, but it is always advisable to know the drug-testing scenario for your sport and to monitor carefully what you give your horse.

Herbs will only test positive to drug testing if the herbal product contains prohibited substances: coffee is an herb that contains caffeine and it will show up on a swab; ephedra is a Chinese herb from which ephedrine was originally derived; and there are many others. However, if you make and use your own herbal preparations, or read labels carefully on proprietary blends, you will not have a problem. There is absolutely no need to use any dangerous herbs to achieve amazing results in either enhancing performance or curing health problems.

The Prepurchase Vet Check

These days much attention is paid to the 'prepurchase vet check'. This is often the case when valuable performance horses are changing hands, and the buyer wants to be sure the animal is in good health before parting with money. In these litigious days, this is probably not surprising. Unfortunately, there *are* unscrupulous 'horse-traders' around and the buyer would indeed do well to be well informed about what s/he is buying. However, one must question the validity and usefulness of the common practice of engaging the services of a vet to perform an (often) expensive exercise, that often does not really draw any firm or reliable conclusions about the horse's suitability for a chosen or proposed career.

X-rays, more often than not, form the basis of the vet's ultimate decision, when evidence of old injuries or purported 'arthritis' is cited as a reason for concern. In actual fact, structural injuries in young and healthy animals (and people) are easy to fix. After all, we were designed to self-repair the knocks to be expected in life and the bones and ligaments will repair and regrow – in all but the most severe cases returning to normal functioning.

Just imagine what the X-ray would show up in the skeleton of a retired rugby or football player. Would you buy him from a picture of his skeleton? If this same sportsman continued to play despite current injuries by using painkillers and otherwise did not allow the injuries to heal properly, he would almost certainly have arthritic problems later in life. If, however, each injury was treated with herbs and rested properly and then rebuilt with exercise, there is no reason why he should have any more problems than the rest of us later in life. The same is true for horses.

The natural repair process will leave signs of scarring that will show up on an X-ray but if full strength and range of movement is available after recovery, there is no reason to fear it is not possible to maintain this. Degeneration is not inevitable. The X-ray will really never replace good judgment, so if the vet says, "my experience tells me you could run into problems later on" and s/he has the relevant experience, listen to the advice. If the vet is looking at an X-ray in search of some textbook standard of perfection, without full knowledge of the animal's history and circumstances, that is entirely unreasonable and no reason to discount a possible purchase.

You would be far more sensible to look at how and where the horse has been cared for prior to purchase, this will tell you much more in terms of his future viability. Herbal feed supplements, comfrey leaf and linseed oil poultices, Bach Flower Rescue Remedy, natural exercise programs and allowing the horse's own pain experience to govern the levels of exercise are all positives. Bute used injudiciously, concrete stable floors, commercial feeds and steroids, are all negatives. Many bone problems are preventable and can be traced back to treatment and training.

Rather than relying on a vet check and X-rays when contemplating a purchase, be more concerned about finding out the history of treatment of past lame episodes or injuries and finding out how and where the horse has been kept.

6 Herbs and Breeding

The reproduction and rearing practices for horses in our modern society is very much a mixture of the traditional wisdom and twentieth century interference. One positive for the equine breeding industry, however, is that, unlike dairy cattle, horses are serviced naturally in the main and foals are left with the mares after foaling, reared in the open and suckled naturally.

The unnatural practices that occur in the equine breeding industry revolve around the timing of the breeding season, in the rearing of youngsters and in the desire for 'purpose-built' horses that defy nature's rules. There is much importance based on the horse's birthday and the performance industries wishing to produce 'older' two-year-olds. It is clear that the older a two-year-old, the better able he is to stand up to the rigors of breaking and training but the hormonal intervention required to produce season in the dams on demand and the workload for the stallion are problematic for their health. In addition, the progeny are often subjected to excessive mental and physical strain long before they are mature enough to cope with it.

The other ingredients of 'intervention madness' in the equine breeding industries surface where the might of money and human egos seem to have taken over from any vestiges of intelligence. We are breeding racehorses solely for speed and wondering why they break down from conformational defects; we are breeding Arabians that look stunning but that no one can ride; we are breeding over-muscled, incredibly pretty Quarter Horses with tiny feet that never make it out of the halter ring. We are even breeding with defective genes that threaten the viability of breeds (the Arabian immune-deficiency disease and HYPP [hyperkalemic periodic paralysis] in Quarter Horses, for example) because breeding stock is too valuable to sterilize. Herbs cannot fix these aberrations but common sense can.

So, recommendations for the equine breeding industry: supply appropriate herbal support for the mare, stallion and the young horse; add a large dash of common sense; blend in a heap of compassion; and subtract the driving force of financial gain. In an ideal world this might be possible but let us start with some suggestions for herbal support, horsekeeping practices and common sense.

The Stallion

Stallions have special needs when it comes to horsekeeping because of the importance of maintaining their virility and potency and because of the conditions in which they are often kept. Herbal preparations can be useful in helping to balance the stallion emotionally and in maintaining optimum levels of potency and virility.

Valuable stallions are often locked up in stables or small stallion yards, not allowed to run free with other horses, not ridden and not socialized to any degree because they are considered 'difficult' to manage. Then, after leading a life of virtual isolation, at the onset of the breeding season they are frequently overworked, manhandled and often panicked during service. The whole process becomes self-perpetuating – as the stallion's behavior worsens, the handlers leave them more to their own devices – until often they become quite unbalanced and sometimes dangerous.

The common excuse for this cycle of mismanagement is that the breeding stallion is too valuable to risk running free with mares and is considered too dangerous to ride. In actual fact, the well-balanced, well-handled stallion – given judicious discipline – will be far more valuable if he is kept in a more natural manner. A badly behaved stallion will be far more tractable if exercised and handled regularly; better still if he has a couple of mares to hang out with in an open pasture, with all the facilities nature can offer: fresh green pasture, shade, trees and water. A big change in a stallion's behavior can even be brought about by situating his yard on a high place with a view of the property – in particular his mares. As well as making him easier to get along with, diminishing stress levels by improving the stallion's lifestyle also has the added advantage of making him far more virile for many years.

The stallion is not just valuable sperm on legs and, paradoxically, realizing this is the first step in making him even more valuable! There are major financial rewards for the stallion owner and major quality-of-life rewards for the stallion to be found in better management. Stallions were born to serve mares and designed to serve frequently, right through their prime and beyond. Low sperm counts, lack of interest and all the related problems that can beset a stallion far too early in his career, are probably all due to stress and a lack of understanding of the nutritional requirements of his work. In addition to making his environment as natural as possible and following horse-friendly handling practices, regular use of herbs for the stallion can be of great benefit to the breeder.

Stallion Herbs

The stallion will derive great benefit from parsley and rosehips (again!) for the iron, the vitamin C and the kidney support (a cup of dried parsley and a third of a cup of rosehip granules a day prepared as an herbal tea as per the instructions in Chapter 2: Making Herbal Teas) but this time especially for the support of his adrenal glands. Borage (a cup of the dried herb added to the tea) is also useful for adrenal support. These herbs are wonderful for the breeding stallion because a healthy and sustainable sex drive comes from a tank full of adrenaline. Bursts of healthy stress – joy, exuberance, challenge and excitement – all release adrenaline into the system and in a healthy stallion this serves to improve his keenness and performance. His adrenaline is released and used up, then the tank is recharged and he is ready again. However, prolonged unhealthy stress depletes adrenaline – it is as simple as that – so you can see the benefit in keeping the stallion's environment as natural and as stress free as possible.

Other herbs to include in a stallion support mixture are the appropriate nervine for that particular horse (see Chapter 4: Nerve Tonics), plus chamomile (in his herbal tea) for the digestive system and for parasympathetic nervous-system support. He also needs dandelion and nettle (a cup of each in his herbal tea), kelp (available for him to free 'graze') and half a cup of some kind of vegetable oil in his diet, along with a source of phyto-hormones like soy (a cup of soy bean meal a day added to feed), or red clover or sarsaparilla (a cup of either added to his herbal tea).

It is difficult to provide a specific generic stallion mixture as it depends so much on the nervous-system type and the history and life experience of the individual stallion. However, the common herbs above would be of great benefit in a stallion's daily feed program. If your stallion has specific needs or problems, an individual mixture needs to be prescribed by a professional herbalist.

The Broodmare

In Australia the breeding season is generally September to December whereas, in nature, horses would come into season between November and February. This, along with the protocol at many stud farms, means that many mares are artificially brought into season using hormone injections.

Stud practices in Australia vary widely, but statistics from the racing industry show that 'wastage' is higher here than in both the UK and the USA and that in recent years it has increased. In Australia only 60 of 100 mares served produce foals, 17% of these foals die before twelve months of age and only 30% of the survivors actually race. That is, fifteen racing progeny are produced in this country for every 100 mares served.

As individual owners seeking to breed we can improve our own mares' prospects markedly by carefully selecting our breeding mares and stallions; by considering other factors than simply performance; by carefully selecting the stud we choose; and by managing the preparation for service and the pregnancy, delivery and rearing ourselves. The best we can do to help alleviate the problems associated with artificial hormonal stimulation and out-of-season breeding is to prepare our dam to minimize the shock of such procedures and to prepare her health as far as possible beforehand.

Bach Flower Rescue Remedy

Bach Flower Rescue Remedy is a homeopathic shock treatment. Simply speaking, it dramatically reduces the destructive energy of shock and really should be given before and after any sort of injection or surgery and after any injury or fall. Bach Flower Rescue Remedy is given orally and only 5-6 drops are necessary for each dose.

The ramifications of shock (both large and small) on future health are very poorly understood by modern medicine and treatment is only considered for the most major types of trauma. Naturopathically, we worry about all shocks large and small and a simple injection or inoculation can produce a large enough shock to affect the whole future health of an animal (or person).

For the broodmare, Bach Flower Rescue Remedy should be given at all stages of preparation for cycling, breeding and foaling and this, along with other nervous-system tonics for a nervous disposition (see Chapter 4: Nervous Types), greatly improve the chances of success. You cannot overdose with Bach Flower Rescue Remedy, the mare cannot become immune to its effects and small, frequent doses can do nothing but good.

Diet

The best physical preparation for the mares going to stud is to make sure they are in 100% good health before attempting to breed. This includes, of course, making sure that any hormonal-type supplements are well and truly out of the system. Since it is very difficult to be sure exactly what chemicals are involved in prepared feed and what their interactions could be, it is much safer to bring breeding stock onto a completely natural diet for a couple of months before attempting to breed. This means clean pasture and clean dry feed, with the minimum of chemical interference.

Herbs and Supplements

Raspberry leaf is the single best herbal preparation for pregnancy and foaling, followed closely by kelp. Parsley is another useful tonic to help the mare to fall pregnant. As a matter of routine, give half a cupful of dried raspberry leaf daily mixed into dry feed for the whole of the preparation time and right through to weaning for all breeding stock. It would also be a good idea to encourage raspberry bushes in an area of your breeding and foaling pastures or in all hedgerows, so that horses can self-medicate if their instincts lead them toward the herb.

Kelp is a cellular feeder and absorbs directly into each cell, it contains nutrients from the ocean and therefore contains all trace elements in organic compounds that can be easily absorbed by the body. Kelp is often prescribed as a supplement for horses and a variety of products and preparations are available. The only caution is that the dose levels recommended are almost always many times higher than necessary – a teaspoonful in feed daily is more than enough.

Iron and vitamin C are part of any build-up program and, although both these nutrients are high in fresh green pasture (especially parsley), one third of a cup of rosehips brewed in boiling water and added to drinking water is a simple, cheap and powerful supplement for a brood mare. Give no other vitamins, minerals or supplements to a healthy mare during the lead-up to breeding and after foaling; raspberry leaf, kelp, parsley and rosehips will do the whole job.

Endeavor to keep your mare at home and take her to the stud for each service. Then, manage her pregnancy, delivery and the rearing of your foal yourself. This dramatically improves your chances of producing a healthy, physically and emotionally balanced foal for whatever intended purpose. If this ideal is not possible, make sure you know exactly, and in great detail, the practices of the stud to which you choose to send your mare. Select a stud much more on the basis of these practices and procedures than simply on the name and performance history of the stallion offered.

The Youngster

If the mare has been maintained in the manner mentioned above, then your chances of having and rearing a healthy foal are already good. Basically, in rearing the young horse, you begin as you mean to continue. Leave the foal on his dam as long as possible – most mares will decide the best time to wean him (after all, they have been doing it successfully for 60 million years, so what on earth makes us think we can improve on nature's system?).

If possible, allow him to play and associate with other mares and youngsters to teach him 'herd politics' as this is the very best way to have a well-adjusted, happy foal. Handle him but be careful not to abuse his trust or to make a pet of him: earn his respect, not his fear or disdain. There are many wonderful books on natural horsemanship and foal handling to help out here but suffice to say that if you follow a sensible training regimen from the very beginning, there will not be any nasty 'breaking' shocks in store for him down the track.

As soon as he starts to eat hard feed (the same cautions apply here as usual, i.e. keep it as natural as possible), you can begin to introduce herbs into his diet: herbs to support his physical growth and immune system (rosehips, garlic, linseed, millet, yarrow and comfrey [see Chapter 2: Preparing Herbs and Chapter 4: Natural Tonics]) and the appropriate nervines (you will be able to identify his temperament early [see Chapter 4: Nerve Tonics]) to support his nervous system. This will help to build a strong young horse and prepare him mentally for his future education.

He should be monitored closely as he grows for any knocks or injuries, which should be treated immediately with arnica cream, comfrey ointment and linseed oil externally. Fanaticism at this stage will create a healthy, resilient mature horse – a 'superhorse' in terms of his general health and performance ability!

When it comes to starting and training the young horse – usually as a two-year-old – take great care to minimize any stress (physical and mental). The later you can leave starting him the better. In actual fact, most two-year-olds have not matured enough for their bones to stand up to the work often given to performance horses at that age. Breaking-in, shoeing, stabling, working on hard surfaces and preparing horses for performance sports such as racing as two-year-olds, is like taking ten-year-old children and, while denying them any time to play, starting them in rigorous training for marathon road running or weightlifting.

Minimize your young horse's exposure to chemicals and avoid injections. Avoid also the pressures and abuses often heaped upon youngsters. Two of these scenarios are worth mentioning here: the

Thoroughbred yearling sales and halter (or in-hand) competition. For both – because large amounts of money are often involved – many breeders are prepared to do whatever it takes (drugs, particularly steroids, unsuitable and too much exercise, inappropriate handling) to produce a muscled, mature-looking youngster. These young horses are also often subjected to a rigorous handling routine that does absolutely nothing for their mental wellbeing. This artificially built up young horse may look good for a short time but do not assume he will be a good long-term prospect, he is in reality a ticking health time-bomb.

The bottom line with the young horse is to be aware that you are creating the foundation for the type of mature horse you want. He is not a disposable item (kept sensibly he could be around for more than 30 years), so begin as you mean to go on with handling, training, feeding, herbal support and a healthy environment.

7 Herbs and Traveling

We all know people who get carsick, airsick or seasick and there are undoubtedly a few horses that get motion sickness in a similar sort of way. Horses traveling long distances are also at risk of respiratory problems, often brought on by their inability to get their heads down in a trailer or truck to drain mucus. The difference between horses and humans is that people rarely, if ever, die or have their career ruined as a result of travel-related illness, but this is a very real risk with horses. Interestingly, some horses can be severely stressed by a three-hour trip; while some carriers regularly transport horses right across continents and deliver them in perfect condition every time, proving that travel need not necessarily be a trauma.

We take our animals to shows, events, studs, trainers or new places all the time. We spend enormous amounts of energy and money preparing them for their sport and bringing them to a peak for the big event, so we should spend an equivalent amount of effort in making sure we do not 'blow it' during one such trip.

In planning for a trip – of whatever duration and whether you are hauling yourself or having a carrier transport your horse – preparation is the most critical element. This includes: making sure your horse is comfortable with the trailer or truck and trailering in general; making sure the actual trailer or truck is safe and as comfortable for the horse as possible; following safe trailering principles and allowing the horse rest breaks; making sure your horse's health is at optimum levels prior to the trip and knowing what signs to look for in case of illness or unease; choosing the right carrier and making sure they are aware of your requirements; and administering herbal treatments prior, during and after a trip to minimize trauma.

Worst-case Traveling Scenarios

The dangers of transporting horses are many and these are a few of the scenarios that can occur if care is not taken: your horse can be flung down, jammed under, hung over or otherwise trapped or injured by the partitions through the actions of a 'cowboy' driver (and that includes yourself); your horse can be asphyxiated, dehydrated, overheated or chilled by poor design or management of ventilation or rugging; or your horse can become panicked and remain in a state of panic for a period of many hours in the worst possible case.

Any of these experiences are likely to result in colic, high temperature, extreme dehydration, extreme stiffness in the limbs, respiratory problems, no interest in feed, water or life in general and require immediate first-aid treatment with Bach Flower Rescue Remedy or an herbal trauma treatment. Such experiences can lead to pneumonia as a secondary infection or develop into stress founder. Any carrier who regularly delivers a horse in bad condition should be named to everyone you speak to whenever talking about horse transport and your personal ambition should be to take care that your horses never have a single bad traveling experience.

Training

The first thing to do with a new or a young horse is to get their confidence in loading and unloading and generally being in and around trailers. It is also a good idea to go through this sort of retraining for any horse that has had a bad experience with trailering. The aim is always to make the experience relaxed and to gain the horse's confidence in loading, unloading and hauling. If you do not feel confident in teaching him this yourself, employ the services of an experienced natural horsemanship trainer to teach you and your horse. Trailering problems are very common and the best way to avoid them is to have your horse trained to be relaxed and confident in a traveling situation. Then, even if someone else hauls him, he is more likely to remain calm.

Practice trips with loading and unloading at breaks along the way are an essential part of trailer training, as all trips should be broken every three hours and the horse unloaded to have a little fresh green pasture, a walk around and something to drink.

Trailer/Truck Design

Argument over design and loading configuration will go on forever. The bottom line is, do not assume that a well-known brand of trailer is necessarily well designed. You cannot buy a well-designed wheelbarrow anymore and we have been making them for hundreds of years!

The requirements for a safe trailer or truck should include the following:

- Access should be quick and simple and there should be room to maneuver if necessary once on board. You should be able to get to a horse's head quickly upon stopping to calm or reassure him after any sort of incident along the way that could cause panic and the head space should not be claustrophobic.
- Ventilation should be plentiful, adjustable and circulate freely about the head area but not cause a chilling draft about the body.
- Temperature should be manageable through airflow and rugging and each individual horse will have his own requirements.
- Flooring must be in good condition and provide drainage and plenty of grip, with no possibility of becoming slippery whatever happens inside. Woven rubber matting, or a bed of fresh shavings on top of the rubber floor, are a couple of good alternatives.
- Partitioning must be very strong and positioned to provide support to the body but must not extend so low that it interferes with the legs at

all. It must provide lateral support but not encourage the horse to travel leaning up against it. There must be no possibility of the horse getting hung up over, or jammed under, partitions if he falls or panics during a trip.

- Room for the horse to brace while the trailer travels is crucial. If a horse cannot brace for a corner without his feet coming up against a wall or standing on another horse's feet, he will quickly and quite naturally, become distressed or worse. This is what creates 'scramblers'.

- Regular maintenance – especially attention to the state of the floor and the suspension – is often overlooked. Make sure the braking system works efficiently and smoothly.

- Whether you should load facing to the rear, to the front or diagonally is arguable – all have their proponents with the rear-facing positioning being favored recently. Common sense dictates that a horse would be better able to brace against a sudden stop if he were facing to the rear and thereby be better protected from a bad driver. You will have horses that will show you their own preferences as to how they like to travel – accommodate them if you can.

Private Transportation

- Prepare your horses properly with traveling boots, leg padding or tail bandages if required.

- Plan long journeys with regular wayside stops no more than three hours apart. Plan to have extra time in hand for extra breaks or unforeseen problems along the way.

- Look out for and use good and safe stopping places along the way. Get the horses off, give them a drink and let them have a walk about and possibly a pick of grass. Many horses that do not like to urinate in the trailer will happily wait if they know you will be stopping regularly.

- Check and clean the floor of the trailer, take out the manure, smooth over the bedding.

- Take note of the frequency of manure evacuation, no manure when expected can be the first sign of colic.

- Take note of the temperature and ventilation and check the horses when you first board the trailer for any signs of temperature distress.

- Hydration is very important while traveling and feed much less so. You should be most aware of the horse's consumption and attitude toward water offered. Some animals prefer water from home (in this case – bring it) others will appreciate a treat with molasses in the water (if this helps to get water into them – do it).
- If you are following a special travel preparation program (see page 136), add the herbal travel mix to the water at each stop. If there is any distress add Bach Flower Rescue Remedy or an herbal trauma mix (ingredients to follow) to the water, or feed it directly over the tongue.
- If there are any suspicions of colic developing, dehydration or nervous distress give the appropriate treatments, spend the time required exercising and comforting the horse and extend the break.

Commercial Transportation

Interview your carrier and ask about their equipment, the route, when and where the scheduled stops will be and expect to be convinced that s/he knows what s/he is doing. If the carrier has not come recommended to you by someone you know who has had first-hand experience, ask to be provided with names and phone numbers of people who have used their services regularly. Call a couple of these people. If you have any doubts whatsoever, look around for alternatives or consider taking the horse yourself.

Provide the carrier with adequate rugs or blankets, any special herbal travel mixture or trauma mixture and instructions as to dosage. Above all, provide contact telephone numbers so that you can be advised of any problems developing along the way. All carriers now carry mobile phones and there is no excuse for an unreported problem.

Arrange to be at the destination yourself, or have the horse met by someone else on arrival and make it clear to the carrier that you will pay the account only upon your animal's delivery in good condition.

If, while making any of these detailed arrangements, you have any doubts, go back to square one. Once a horse has had a bad experience or gone down they will lose confidence and become bad travelers thenceforth. When a horse has become a nervous traveler he will always use up heaps of adrenaline and nervous energy during a trip, which you would rather have available for your competition.

Herbal Travel Treatments

Trauma Treatments

If your horse has an accident or trauma while traveling, swift treatment and support can be invaluable. Any extreme of shock, whether physical or emotional, requires urgent treatment to prevent the subsequent effects of such shock; Bach Flower Rescue Remedy treatment is the very first thing that should be administered immediately after any trauma. This can be administered as just a couple of drops in the mouth or in the eye and is best administered before the horse is moved at all. Take a dose yourself when coming upon a distressed animal to help you settle and to make better decisions.

Blends of suitable herbs can also help an animal recover more fully from trauma. These blends would include herbal treatments for nervous and adrenal exhaustion, for kidney function in the case of dehydration, for heart stress in the case of prolonged panic and for the immune system, which always suffers as a result of stress. Homeopathic treatments should also be included to minimize the effects of the trauma on the animal's trust, confidence and subsequent reaction to travel, competition or tolerance to stress in general.

Preventative Treatments

A professional herbalist will formulate herbal travel mixes for individual animals that take into account their own personality and experience. These consist of herbal extracts or decoctions to build up an animal's reserves to ensure he is in the best possible shape to cope with the stress of travel. Based on previous chapters, you should have built up an understanding of your own horse's personality and metabolism that will give you a good indication of the pretravel treatment regimen to follow for him.

The preventative treatment you give your horse may be as simple as just adding cold rosehips tea to drinking water for the trip to ensure that his kidney function is maintained and adrenal glands are well protected from depletion.

For animals that do not travel well, or are so valuable or so highly placed in their field that absolutely no chances whatsoever can be taken with spoiling any of their physical or emotional form during travel, you will need a much more sophisticated personalized mixture. This will include: herbs to minimize any chances of digestive-system problems like scouring or colic; herbs to protect kidneys and adrenal glands from stress; herbs to nourish and strengthen the nervous system to allow the fearful horse to be relaxed and comfortable on the trip; herbs to build up the immune system to ensure there is no physical loss of form or likolihood of contracting an infection; and homeopathic treatments to treat any weakness areas in the individual animal's reaction patterns (fearfulness, apprehension, self-confidence, tendency to panic etc.).

These individual comprehensive treatments are given for a couple of weeks before, during and for a few days after, a major relocation, or the day before and during a normal weekend trip.

Herbal Ingredients

The following list is by no means comprehensive but it includes most of the herbs to consider for inclusion in preparations to treat travel-related trauma, or for protecting horses from all possible negative effects of travel.

Combine a cup each of the following dried herbs made into a tea (see Chapter 2: Making Herbal Teas):

Rosehips are a valuable herb extremely high in iron and vitamin C and especially useful to protect the body from kidney and adrenal exhaustion occasioned by fear or panic.

Vervain is a particularly effective treatment for a horse that tends to be agitated, fidgety and 'nervy' generally. Such a horse is more likely to panic or lose his cool if unexpected things happen during a trip; giving vervain before and during a trip will help him to cope with the experience.

Hops are another nervous-system herb to include in a travel mixture because it deals with another aspect of the panicky, nervous disposition found in many horses. The best possible support for the nervous-system during a trip will leave more nervous energy 'in the tank' for the competition.

Chamomile is the primary digestive and parasympathetic nervous-system support herb. Chamomile administered prior to stress, or regularly to a horse prone to colic, is the best preventative treatment for this condition. There is no excuse for colic resulting from travel – it is always a reflection of poor preparation or handling.

Dandelion and agrimony are liver-support herbs, which, along with chamomile, may help reduce the chances of scouring occurring due to stress. Scouring will aggravate dehydration problems, is debilitating in itself and the watery manure can make footing more difficult and lead to a fall in the trailer if the floor becomes slippery. Dandelion will also play a role in preventing colic from developing during a trip.

Add 50 ml of **hawthorn berry** extract (carry a bottle of extract with you when traveling as well): hawthorn is a major heart tonic especially suitable for horses and is the second thing to reach for when coming upon a distressed horse (ten drops in water or over the tongue) – the first being Bach Flower Rescue Remedy. Hawthorn is your best bet to bring back a severely abused animal (such as a horse that has been down and/or in a panic for hours while someone has continued to drive).

Add 10 ml of **maritime pine** extract. This extract is an antioxidant fifteen or twenty times more powerful than vitamin C or vitamin E, which can build up your and your horse's immunity more than any single other substance. Its application in a travel mix is to give your horse's immunity a huge boost, so that any stress that can cause depletion is countered immediately.

Add twenty drops each of the following **Bach Flower Remedies**: The flower remedies to consider are all those involved in change, fear, exhaustion, apprehension, panic, shock etc. and would therefore include: aspen, rock rose, mimulus, Bach Flower Rescue Remedy, wild rose, olive, walnut and larch.

Add a cup of the resulting mix to the horse's feed morning and night.

Travel trauma to horses can be prevented, or at the very least minimized, if proper preparation is undertaken. This is true of a trip between suburbs, a weekend event in the country, a trip across the continent or, indeed, a trip across the world.

8 Sharing Herbs With Your Horse

We presume that by this stage you have developed a real feel for treating your horse with herbs. The good news is, you have also developed a feel for treating yourself! In fact, there are enormous benefits to be obtained by sharing your horse's herbs.

The most dramatic area showing the benefits of taking the same herbal mixture as you are giving your horse is in the treatment of nervous complaints. A common occurrence in the horse world is the highly-strung horse paired with the highly-strung owner, particularly in the show and dressage fields. Quite often the best results are achieved when the horse and the owner share the herbal mix!

We all know that the communication between our horses and ourselves is some combination of training, physical and voice cues and often something quite indefinable. We usually know how our horse is feeling and he knows how we are feeling and this emotional communication can be just as important as anything else in a competition situation. In the light of this knowledge, sharing remedies with your horse makes a lot of sense and has proved to be very effective.

In recommending herbs for horses and owners, it is important to assess the whole situation. For example, in the case of a champion dressage horse that has become uncharacteristically willful, obstinate or contrary, a herbalist would need to assess all the factors that may have led to this change. This will include questions about the animal's personality and a whole health, ownership and training history. By the time you have all those details; you also have a good idea of the owner's nature, which may also be influenced by their own particular health and circumstances at the time. As with breaking into a chronic health or behavior pattern of a child, it is important to treat the mother as well, to allow the habitual pattern of action and reaction to readjust itself. So it is with horses and riders.

The herbs that could be suggested in the case of the above dressage horse could be hops and valerian for the horse and, perhaps, vervain and hops for the rider; so you would put all three in a common mix, made up as a tea (see Chapter 2: Making Herbal Teas). You would also include Bach Flower Remedies (twenty drops of each) to manage the emotional relationship and reactions. These could include vine for the willfulness of both and aspen and larch for the confidence and apprehension that may be a common underlying factor. In addition you could probably include other Bach Flower Remedies such as walnut and wild oat, which would facilitate the movement toward establishing a new and more comfortable working relationship. To support this remedy, it would be a good idea to have the owner making up both rosehips and chamomile tea for both herself and the horse, which would serve to recharge the adrenal reserves and settle the digestive upsets they both experience under stress. It is easy to see why approaching the problem holistically like this is far more likely to produce a lasting positive result than using any sort of proprietary product either chemical or herbal.

Aside from the nervous-system case described, there is an almost unlimited variety of other nervous combinations in horse and rider that respond to joint treatment and each one is an interesting challenge in itself. Other examples of when to have horse and rider on the same mix are in the top levels of endurance or eventing competition, when a herbalist might prescribe a common treatment program for horse and rider just to compensate for the wear and tear of such grueling events. For an arthritic horse and rider team it is usual to make up a common mix to make the day's riding or competition more comfortable and enjoyable for them both. For a team that has trouble keeping their immune systems up to scratch, horse and rider may end up sharing their rosehips, pine bark, garlic, yarrow, echinacea, fenugreek and lemon combinations to protect their immunity before very high levels of competition, when performing poorly due to 'athletes flu' might cost a medal.

Herb sharing can help horse and owner stay in step

Over the years, it is become more and more obvious that we can share many things with our horses, not the least being herbal remedies. So once you have established a herbal preventative and treatment regimen for your equine partner, you might like to take a look at your own needs; you will likely find the herbal solutions already in your barn.

9 Herbs and the Other Therapies

The use of herbs for healing with horses is certainly not self-exclusive. We have already looked at the importance of treating the whole horse and today there is a large range of non-invasive, alternative treatments available to horse owners for maintaining the health and wellbeing of their charges. Careful use of these other modalities – homeopathic treatments, chiropractic, massage etc. – is complementary to the healing power of herbs. In an ideal world, we would have access to, and the knowledge to apply, the whole gamut of treatments for the greater good. In an ideal world, we would also have vets and all the other equine health practitioners all working side by side – this is occurring more and more and is certainly a worthwhile aim.

Let us look briefly now at some of the other complementary treatments and their value for use in conjunction with herbs.

Homeopathy and Bach Flowers

Homeopathy

The use of homeopathic substances is a healing art that has its roots in the seventeenth century and one that has been adopted with great success by health practitioners all over the world in recent times. Animals have been found to have particularly positive responses to the use of homeopathy (perhaps because they have no ingrained preconceptions or prejudices).

Homeopathy is often considered strange and 'unscientific' because essentially a homeopathic dilution of a substance contains nothing much more than the vibrational energy of that substance. It has been diluted until all the physical presence of the original substance has been diluted out of it. However, homeopathic remedies react with the energy of the horse's (or human's) system and are capable of extremely profound and powerful effects.

The genesis of this science was in the heyday of 'medicine by poisons', when very strong poisons or irritant substances were in vogue, patients being dosed with arsenic, mercury, antimony, opium etc. It was observed in those days that highly diluted solutions of these substances produced the opposite effect to their full-strength counterparts. The observers then began experimenting and found that it seemed to be universally true that if a particular poison caused a certain set of physical symptoms, then a homeopathic concentration of the same substance would remove the same set of symptoms, however caused, in a patient. The underlying premise is 'like can treat like' – hence the name 'homeopathy'.

A crude example could be something like this: for a human patient, two carrots juiced are a useful source of vitamin A, while two bags of juiced carrots would cause vitamin A poisoning with subsequent damage to the liver and other systems. It therefore follows (homeopathically) that a highly diluted material made from carrots would be useful in two ways: to cure a severe case of vitamin A poisoning; and to stimulate the metabolic processes within the body relating to vitamin A.

Homeopathic concentrations are made by taking small amounts of material in tincture form and diluting them down sequentially as follows: ten drops of tincture in 100 ml of alcohol and water mix, which is then shaken in a particular way. Ten drops of this mix is then added to a fresh 100 ml of alcohol and water and the procedure repeated – 3 times, 6 times, 30 times, 60 times, 100 times, 1000 times etc. – all producing different dilutions and all working slightly differently and increasingly profoundly. Homeopathic preparations are labeled with 3X, 100X, 30C (the C-rating designates stronger potency) etc. to designate the dilution.

There are very good homeopathic materia medica available that list a large number of the different preparations and the conditions/symptoms for which they are used, with the appropriate dilutions to use for various conditions. These books are available for humans, horses and even dogs and cats, are excellent references to have on the bookshelf, and are fairly easy to follow.

Treatments are available in pillule form when the ingredient is contained in a small sugar granule (excellent for administering to horses), or liquid form, which can be dropped on the tongue or added to drinking water or feed. The dilutions most commonly used for horses are 6X, 12X, 30X and 200X – depending on the condition and the individual horse – and a good homeopathic materia medica will provide instructions. Essentially, only one dose of a homeopathic preparation is required to effect a rebalancing of the metabolism, although it is often a good idea to continue the homeopathic treatment for as long as the herbs for specific conditions, to make sure the horse has actually had sufficient contact with the remedy.

Common treatments

Following is a short list of some of the main homeopathic remedies that are helpful in treating horses when used in conjunction with herbs:

Aconitum is useful in any condition involving acute, sudden onset of symptoms – particularly fever, inflammation or respiratory distress – given in the early stages. Useful for any condition where the horse is suffering from severe anxiety, e.g. the early stages of colic.

Apis mellifica is used for any condition involving swelling or edema of the skin and hot burning itch (when skin, joints etc. are puffy and tender to the touch).

Arnica is a major remedy (which has similar actions to the Bach Flower Rescue Remedy) for any trauma or shock.

Arsenicum is for any condition causing exhaustion or debilitation, especially when the horse is also exhibiting signs of restlessness and increased thirst for small amounts of water. An excellent aid to healing after trauma, surgery or in the case of a debilitating illness. Also a useful remedy for scours, if the stools are watery.

Belladonna is useful for any condition that comes on quickly, involving inflammation, mental excitement, nervousness or fear. Also useful where the horse has an elevated, bounding pulse rate, dilated pupils, or a reduced thirst. Helpful for the early stages of colic.

Bryonia is a remedy used for conditions that are worsened by movement and that come on slowly.

Hepar sulph is used when the horse is suffering from extreme sensitivity to pain and shows a tendency to inflammation and pus formation in the respiratory system and the skin (often any small injury will become infected). The horse that needs this remedy will also often be excessively thirsty.

Hypericum is a good remedy to have on hand in case of accident or illness involving intense pain (especially associated with injury to nerves or soft structures). It is also useful in treating the symptoms of tetanus.

Kali bich is excellent for respiratory conditions (usually long-standing) where there is tough stringy mucus involved and phlegm in bronchial tubes that is difficult for the horse to expel.

Nux vomica helps in the treatment of constipation and diarrhea, particularly if the horse has eaten indigestible feed. Can also be helpful in treating colic if the attack is related to eating indigestible feed.

Pulsatilla is helpful for treating conditions where there is a thick nasal discharge. This is often the remedy for the sensitive, timid, easily-upset horse.

Rhus tox is a useful remedy for painful conditions of joints or ligaments that improve with exercise; also excellent to give a horse suffering from over-exertion.

The above list is minimal, consult a homeopath or specialist books on the subject for a more comprehensive overview. There is also a range of powerful homeopathic remedies available for treating and avoiding specific conditions such as tetanus, specific bacteria, specific viruses, etc. These are valuable alternatives to injections and conventional vaccinations, but it is best to consult a veterinary homeopath with regards to administering these remedies.

Bach Flowers

The Bach Flower Remedy essences are homeopathic formulations that directly unwind or cancel energy spirals characteristic of emotional states and, as such, are a perfect complement to the physiological effects of ingesting herbs. This combining of homeopathic and herbal remedies was pioneered by internationally-renowned herbalist, natural therapist and author, Dorothy Hall (my teacher), thirty or more years ago – much to the discomfort of purists from both camps. Through her influence, however, and the successes of practitioners trained in her system of prescribing such combinations, this technique is much more widely accepted nowadays.

In purchasing the Bach Flower Remedies (from most health-food shops, naturopaths, many herbalists and some specialist pharmacies), bear in mind that one drop of the concentrated stock (the original undiluted strength) – in the horse's feed, over his tongue, or added to his herbal tea – is usually enough. Technically, you could add one drop to a swimming pool and then one drop from the pool would be as good as one drop of stock (except for the chlorine!). There are radionically (or electronically) prepared Bach Flower Remedies available – but the stock remedies are generally more trustworthy.

Many simple self-explanatory manuals relating to the use of the Bach Flower Remedies are available for horse owners to study. They usually contain an explanation of how the remedies work and a list of the various remedies and their application. The books are mainly written for humans but the application to animals, in most cases, is very similar.

The remedies themselves are completely safe to administer and to experiment with as long as you understand them. It is also important to have specific aims in mind when prescribing and administering them because the way in which you approach giving the remedies has an effect.

There is a curious 'unscientific' aspect to the intentions of the person who administers these remedies that affects the outcome, which is rather like the 'observer effect' being found nowadays in quantum physics experimentation. If you have a clear picture in your mind of the emotional state your horse is currently in and the state you would like him to be in after taking the remedy and you approach him with healing in mind, you have the right intention.

Common Treatments

The following Bach Flower Remedies are useful adjuncts to herbal treatments and the times to apply particular remedies will become second nature with a little practice.

Bach Flower Rescue Remedy should be kept in the house, the barn, the traveling first-aid kit and the saddlebags on a permanent basis. It is the Bach Flower Remedy combination that settles all the emotional components that accompany physical and emotional trauma, including shock, fear, panic and apprehension. It addresses the possibility that the trauma will have physical repercussions (through its effect on the adrenal glands, thyroid and pituitary gland), which could result in potential health problems from that moment forward. In the light of horses' reactive natures, this is a remedy that is particularly effective and one to keep on hand at all times.

Aspen is for apprehension or fear without an object. This is for the horse that spooks at shadows and sees 'gremlins' behind every rock. It is also useful for the horse that seems constantly tense and worried for no discernible reason as if they are thinking, "something is going to get me - I do not know what it is but something bad is just around the corner!".

Cerrato balances out the energy picture which involves a mind that flicks from one thing to another in a distracted pattern and is unable to focus on one course of action long enough to complete it. This horse will often seem to concentrate on what you are teaching him for a short time and then become distracted by different things in his surroundings.

Cherry plum calms the energy of panic and allows a nervous horse to manage his feelings so they do not result in panic and the accompanying random behavior, such as spooking and bolting. This is a great remedy for the horse whose first reaction to any new or unexpected stimulus is unreasoning panic and loss of control.

Clematis is for the horse that has trouble concentrating. This is not so much a remedy for the horse that is busy in the mind (like the white-chestnut horse) but rather for the horse that seems periodically 'off in another world' as if he were daydreaming. He will sometimes seem to be indifferent to you, or 'off with the pixies' when you are asking for his attention. When he is 'with' you, he is often very intuitive to your intentions and wonderfully obliging; out in the pasture such a horse will be able to dissipate stresses more effectively than most and do well. Punishing a clematis horse for a loss in concentration is very confusing for him and counter-productive because he has no idea whatsoever why he is being punished. His random gaps in concentration are very healthy, as they are akin to the meditative state, but frustrating on competition day! A few doses of clematis on the day of an event will hold the horse's attention together through the event.

Crab apple is the remedy to include when there is a sense of 'unclean' about a situation. For example, this could be something like an irritation in a horse's eye, be it a foreign object, pus from an infection or an uncomfortable inflamed appearance. For this reason crab apple is often included in first-aid treatments and in dealing with infections and included in a mixture for blood poisoning or an illness that shows up as ugly sores or spots. Crab apple is also included in nervous-system treatments when the horse exhibits an element of fastidiousness - an unwillingness to get muddy or wet for example. If correctly applied, crab apple will facilitate healing in such situations by allowing the energy of the system to focus on the healing rather than on how the horse (or the rider!) feels about the condition or situation.

Honeysuckle is a Bach Flower Remedy that is particularly useful for ex-racehorses and horses with a history of abuse or poor handling. Honeysuckle will assist the horse to break away from past experiences, which are often a block to training. It is the 'link breaker' and works really well in conjunction with larch and mimulus for a horse where the root cause of handling difficulties goes all the way back to a breaking and handling experience that left him permanently nervous and lacking in confidence.

Impatiens is for the horse (and rider) that leaps before he looks. His mind is rushing ahead of his body and he does not think things through before acting. Impatiens will bring the mind back into line with the job at hand and is very useful for the discipline sports like eventing, dressage and showjumping.

Larch is useful when the underlying problem is really self-confidence. Lack of self-confidence is a characteristic of many domestic horses, particularly those that have been subjected to careless, inappropriate training methods and that have never been rewarded for trying or for a job well done.

Mimulus is for fear with an object. This is the horse that has specific fears such as a fear of trailers, water, blue tarpaulins, ponies pulling carts, black tree stumps in the forest, or any of the many and varied objects that can represent threat in the mind of an equine!

Rock water is another useful remedy to break into a habit pattern, particularly one which is very predictable when you would assess that the horse is very 'set in his ways': a fairly common condition given that horses are notoriously dependent on routine. Emotionally, rock water is similar in its effect as valerian is physically: it will allow a horse to be more fluid and elastic in his attitude.

Walnut is for over-sensitivity. This is useful for the horse that consistently over-reacts, i.e. one that jumps nervously from slight leg pressure or falls to pieces when he does not understand a direction. He is also the horse that needs clear direction from a leader and, in a herd situation, is usually low in the pecking order. Walnut is also fundamental in assisting a horse to cope with a change in circumstances (such as moving) or the adoption of new ideas. It is the most useful of all Bach Flower Remedies, because it smoothes the way during change and retraining. For example, the combination of vine, walnut and sensitive handling will train a horse out of willful habits.

White chestnut is for overly busy mental activity, often resulting in an inability to decide how to act. This is the remedy for the busy-minded horse: one that is constantly looking and reacting to things happening in the next pasture while you are trying to train him; one who cannot seem to decide just what the appropriate response is to a training cue so he runs through his entire repertoire.

Vine is for willfulness. This is the remedy for the horse that thinks he knows better than you and that tries to dominate his handlers and his pasture mates. He will try to make his own decisions while you are training and seems very certain in all his decisions. He is the horse that will sometimes test the boundaries as he seeks to have his own way, he is often obstinate or stubborn and can sometimes just 'shut down' when under stress. You should encourage and positively reinforce this horse around such willpower obstacles rather than insisting. The vine horse does not cope at all well with the harsh traditional breaking practices that use force to mould the horse to the handler's will.

Note Heed the warnings not to expose Bach or other homeopathic remedies to strong sunlight, camphor, perfume, radiation (mobile phones, x-rays at airports) etc. or they will lose their effectiveness.

Other Alternative Therapies

With the advent of the 'alternative revolution', there are a large number of alternative therapies available for the horse owner, ranging from massage and chiropractic, to 'past-life' readings for your horse(!). Many types of massage, acupressure/acupuncture and adjustment techniques are wonderfully complementary to the use of herbs because they work on realigning the horse's life energy in the same way as herbs. Massage and other hands-on techniques are very relaxing for the horse and, if you learn to do these yourself rather than relying on a professional, the massage sessions allow a fantastic time for bonding with your horse.

Along with a general recommendation of support for all the other alternative therapies, we must also include a word of warning. True horse people really genuinely care about their horses and will usually go without food themselves rather than let their horses go hungry (the old saying that 'poverty is owning a horse' is a valid one!). This care (some of the 'unafflicted' call it obsession) makes the caring horse owner somewhat vulnerable to the 'New Age sharks'. As we mentioned in the early sections of the book, the 'alternative revolution' has and will continue to provide a source of considerable income for the smart operator and they are certainly out there among the genuine, sincere, trained professionals. A horse owner who is experiencing seemingly insurmountable health or behavioral problems with a beloved horse is a very susceptible being indeed.

A case we heard about recently involved a lady who had experienced behavioral problems with her horse for the five years she had had him since he was a weanling. After being a clinic and alternative therapy 'groupie' with little success, as a last resort she had engaged the services of a woman who claimed to perform 'past-life' readings for horses. After parting with AU$600 for three sessions, she was informed that the problems she experienced with the horse were the result of the fact that they had been lovers in a past life and that she had betrayed him! All very interesting, however no solutions were offered. Perhaps she would have been better served to determine the horse's nervine type, feed him the appropriate herbs and then follow the same process for herself.

The bottom line for all you do with your horse – and this includes using other complementary therapies – is to use your common sense and your intuition. The more you rely on your instincts as to what is right for you and your horse, the more finely-tuned those instincts will become.

Herbs and Veterinary Science

As we have stressed throughout this book, there are indeed many situations where modern veterinary science prevails. The herbalist's art lies in treating and balancing the whole organism so that it is better able to avoid and combat ill health, not in dealing with the ill health that has become acute, or severe physical injury requiring surgery. When faced with acute situations (for example acute colic, severe wounds or trauma), give the herbal first aid, call the vet immediately and use herbs and other alternative therapies to support the horse through the crisis.

Clients are often concerned about how herbal and alternative treatments will affect any veterinary procedures or medications that may be necessary for their horses (anti-inflammatories, antihistamines, antibiotics, injury treatments, etc.). While it is never advisable to mix and match pharmaceutical drugs *ad hoc*, the considered use of herbs in conjunction with veterinary treatment is extremely beneficial.

Herbal treatments should just be continued throughout whatever is occurring with the horse (recovery, resting, working, etc.), as they will certainly not have an adverse effect on the horse's health. In fact, the opposite is the case and it is often advantageous to prescribe additional support mixtures for a horse going in for an operation or veterinary procedure. This is also true for horses traveling a long distance across the country or overseas, or any other stress-inducing situation. This preventive care greatly reduces the likelihood or severity of problems resulting from stress or shock.

The next often asked question is: "Should I tell my vet I'm using herbal remedies? He might not be comfortable with this". Basically, each client needs to determine what would be appropriate to tell their veterinary practitioners, based on that practitioner's own alternative inclinations. In very many cases, the veterinarians are fascinated and impressed by the results from herbal treatments and it is great to use every opportunity to educate them about herbs and natural therapies; conventional and traditional therapies working side by side is the way of the future, after all.

10 Specific Conditions

While we stress that herbs are not most effectively used as a 'quick fix' for specific named problems, as an easy reference for users, we have listed some common complaints under general headings. However, rather than using the 'medical' formula of Symptom/Disease X = Herb Y, we have outlined which other areas in the horse's management regimen may need attention and suggested supportive herbs that have proved valuable in these cases. As the province of the herbalist is not, in general, in the treatment of conditions that have become acute or life-threatening, we stress that if you are confronted with such a condition, please contact your equine health professional. Bear in mind, however, that should you need to resort to pharmaceutical treatments or surgery, complementary herbal treatments to support your horse's metabolic systems during the illness and throughout recuperation will give him the best possible chance of a full recovery.

Use your knowledge and intuition as it grows in choosing herbs for problems; always look at the 'whole horse' in terms of your complete care regimen and his general health, and do not limit treatment to that listed below if you feel something else might help.

Allergic Reactions

Horses can have an allergic reaction to a variety of bites: spiders, ants, mosquitoes and biting flies to name a few. Allergic reactions can equally often arise through the reaction to unnatural chemical substances, and the most severe or life-threatening reactions are from this area rather than from biting creatures (with the probable exception of snakes, which are common enough in many parts of the world).

The reaction can vary from a slight skin irritation, through the formation of large welts and swelling all over the body, to respiratory distress and worse. Conventional veterinary medicine prescribes antihistamines for the milder cases and emergency first aid like adrenaline or antivenom for the most severe. In these severe cases do not sit around waiting for your herb teas to brew – give Bach Flower Rescue Remedy, take some yourself and call the vet. For the milder cases involving minor skin irritations or swellings not causing respiratory distress, herbs can be very efficacious.

HELPFUL HERBS

Bach Flower Rescue Remedy (4 – 6 drops), chamomile (one cup a day as herbal tea – see Chapter 2: Making Herbal Teas) and horseradish (fresh root, minced: one tablespoon a day in feed) are all commonly useful in the treatment of allergic reactions, with the Bach Flower Rescue Remedy being called for as first aid for a dramatic reaction. Bach Flower Rescue Remedy can save a life in cases of the most serious type of anaphylactic shock reaction (sometimes to drugs) that can be life-threatening.

In professional mixes, comfrey can be included along with euphorbia (which is not recommended for general use). These two herbs each support the spleen in different ways. It is support of the spleen, which is seen from the holistic point of view to be the organ involved in hot and angry responses, in conjunction with the nervous- and immune-system support, which will help to resolve the reaction involved in an allergic response. Doses for these herbs need to be prescribed by a professional herbalist.

Homeopathic treatments (five or six drops twice a day over the tongue) are particularly suited to allergic reactions and it is often efficacious to use a selected few of these for specific reactions. Bach Flower Rescue Remedy is always indicated in these cases, being a combination of five of the Bach Flower Remedies, including walnut for over-sensitivity and holly for angry reaction. The homeopathic remedy apis mellifica, which is derived from the sting of the honeybee, is a specific remedy for an itchy reaction like that of a bee sting. If your horse has a very specific allergic response and you are able to describe it carefully to a qualified homeopath, they can almost certainly match a remedy to the particular case and your problems are over.

Chamomile is included in all situations where the reaction is coming out of the parasympathetic nervous system and/or from over-sensitivity of any sort, so it will help in breaking a pattern of allergy.

The action of horseradish is to assist the body in clearing histamines from the blood and so, although it does not disable the histamines as do the conventional drugs, it offers much better longer-term prospects. With a predictable allergy response, say one that appears at a certain season of the year or flowering of a plant, it is a very good idea to provide horseradish for your horse for a month or six weeks prior to the expected problem time. In this way the histamine levels, which are building up to the point where symptoms begin to appear with just one more exposure, are being cleared more efficiently. Therefore you are able to postpone the reactions, hopefully until later in the season, or even right through the problem time altogether.

If you are able to work through the whole allergy cycle in this preventative way, this will allow the horse to become less and less reactive with each exposure or season. Normally the pattern occurs the other way around because allergies by their very nature tend to build upon the reactivity with each exposure and become more and more chronic over time.

Anemia

A low red blood cell count (anemia) in a performance horse is a concern and a fairly common one in older horses. It is the result of an underlying metabolic dysfunction involving the spleen, the bonemarrow and the management of iron and oxygen levels within the blood.

In many cases, in otherwise healthy animals, the problem can be traced to a weakness within the walls of the venous-system blood vessels, which allows iron and blood products to be lost directly through the blood-vessel walls.

The conventional treatment for this condition is to administer supplements – vitamin injections and additives, even steroids – to increase the oxygen-carrying capability of the blood. Herbal alternatives to this treatment are effective. They are capable of completely resolving the problem and they are cheap and non-injurious to the horse's general health.

PREVENTION

Do not take too many blood samples to verify blood levels – rely on the color of the horse's gums (they should be a healthy pink; not too pale) and his general vitality - as each injection depletes the immunity and each test depletes the pocketbook. It is completely unnecessary to verify treatment constantly with blood tests. It is impossible to manage blood quality by adding supplements to the feed that show up as low in a blood profile (e.g. iron) because all such imbalances are not simply a result of a lack in the diet, but much more to do with how the body manages its resources.

There is a whole multimillion-dollar industry built up around iron tonics and tests for humans and animals built on the mechanistic assumption that iron supplements improve blood quality. Not so. The industry even recommends giving iron supplements to racing greyhounds whose main diet is red meat – imagine that!

Iron supplements, often not being derived from organic sources, are poorly absorbed and they do not address in any way the management of blood quality and iron management at the level of the spleen, the bone marrow and the vascular system as described above.

HELPFUL HERBS

The main herbs to consider for reversing an anemic pattern are kelp, yarrow, nettle, comfrey, rosehips and rue.

Kelp contains all the trace minerals (see Chapter 4: Electrolytes).

Nettle is just dried stinging nettle and is an extremely high source of organic iron, which enriches the iron levels in the blood. This can be fed as a dried herb or you can boil up fresh nettle leaves and stalks and add the resultant brew to drinking water.

Yarrow is also high in iron, but works more to stimulate bone-marrow production of red blood cells. You should be able to grow this for yourself: it is a common pasture weed in Europe and therefore grows well in temperate climates. Yarrow is usually harvested and given to horses as a dried herb, but can be made into a tea as suggested in the treatment of roaring (see page 199).

Comfrey, along with its many other virtues, will stimulate and normalize both spleen and bone-marrow function, so that together with yarrow it has the ability to completely rejuvenate any malfunction in both systems and produce much better blood results. This combination will also reverse many other complex blood quality problems in man and beast, including platelet problems.

Rosehips show up yet again as a supplementary ingredient and supportive tonic to the blood, as well as to many other metabolic systems.

Rue specifically strengthens the walls of the vascular system within the body, especially the venous system, and any weaknesses will be reversed with regular exposure to this herb. The commercial source of rutin, which was originally identified from the herb rue, is buckwheat. This makes the grain a very valuable addition to the diet of a racehorse or an endurance horse, whose circulatory systems are put under considerable strain. Blackcurrants also contain significant amounts of rutin.

All these herbs can be grown in your hedgerow for your horses to choose for themselves.

If making up a specific treatment, combine 500 g each of kelp, borage, nettle, red clover and rue and 1 kg of yarrow. Prepare 1 liter of comfrey root extracted into organic cider vinegar, along with twenty drops of Bach Flower Rescue Remedy (or use two fresh comfrey leaves a day). Prepare 1 liter of hawthorn and maritime pine bark extracted into organic cider vinegar.

Feed one cupful twice a day of the dry herb mixture made into tea and 10 ml twice a day of each of the vinegar-based extracts. Also include 500 ml of rosehips tea twice daily in the horse's feed.

Azoturia (Tying-up)

'Tying-up', the common name for this complaint, is an accurate description of what happens to a horse suffering this condition when, during or after exercise, he will suddenly only be able to move with difficulty and pain as though his hindquarters have been tied up with ropes. Symptoms also often include excessive sweating and muscle tremors in the hindquarters, while sometimes in severe cases the muscles of the forequarters may also be involved.

It is unlikely that azoturia was a condition suffered by wild horses. This is not because the domesticated horse is weaker or necessarily works harder (a stallion in the wild would actually have to work very hard to serve and defend his band of mares) but research suggests that azoturia is a result of the feeding and exercise practices we visit on our domestic horses – specifically high-grain diets and irregular exercise. In earlier times the condition was known as 'Monday morning disease' as work-horses on high-grain diets would suffer an attack after their rest day on Sunday, the sudden onset coming when they resumed their workload.

Physiologically, tying-up is a situation when, during work, lactic acid builds up in the muscles faster than the kidneys are able to clear it out. These muscles go into spasm and many muscles, therefore, end up pulling against each other, which causes the characteristic stiffness and soreness.

Medically, the condition is seen as a kidney problem and is treated using electrolyte or diuretic therapy. Holistically, the problem is a little more complicated and, as usual, a fuller understanding and simple precautions can prevent the problem and can certainly minimize the damage done if tying-up does occur.

Do not accept advice that suggests more electrolytes, diuretics or other chemical medicines will cure the problem of tying-up. These products may mask the pain and other symptoms temporarily but they have no capacity to heal and restore whatsoever - quite the contrary.

PREVENTION

As discussed, it seems that work habits and feeding are the main reasons why the modern horse suffers from this condition when the wild horse probably did not. Following a sensible work and feeding regimen can preclude the condition from happening at all.

Before every single work session the horse should be warmed up by walking first for at least ten minutes, followed by ten minutes of working trot. Mounting a cold horse and immediately asking for strenuous work is unwise and insensitive. Work sessions should have intervals of slow work and walking, which is the best way to build fitness and allow the kidneys and the circulatory and respiratory systems to 'catch up'.

Work sessions should also always allow for a proper cooling down. Establish a routine that includes at least ten to fifteen minutes of warming up and ten minutes of cooling down. Get into the habit of looking at your watch and if you cannot plan sufficient time to include warm-up and cool-down periods, change your own schedule, not the horse's.

With regard to feed, the energy/protein feed (specifically grain) intake should be managed to suit the demands of the horse's work; a horse in light work will not really need grain at all, while a horse in heavy work will require more. A horse requires much less of this sort of feed on days off but more to cover extended periods of exertion such as those required for endurance, polo and eventing. Bearing in mind your horse's type and the activity he undertakes, take care not to over-feed the energy/protein component of his rations.

Sound management of feeding and exercise routines will minimize the likelihood of tying-up and simple herbal remedies can further protect and rehabilitate the horse's kidney function.

As a preventative measure, make sure your horse has access at all times to sea salt and kelp and receives rosehips as part of his daily feed regimen (see Chapter 4: Electrolytes).

HELPFUL HERBS

At the first signs of your horse tying-up during exercise, you should stop work, administer Bach Flower Rescue Remedy, cool the horse down by leading him at a walk for at least half an hour and then maintain his body temperature by hosing in the summer and covering with blankets in the winter. When you have settled him down, you should drench him with an herbal tea made from both rosehips and dandelion (see Chapter 2: Making Herbal Teas) and give him further doses of Bach Flower Rescue Remedy (5–10 drops over the tongue). Then put him out in a grassy pasture so he can forage and exercise himself gently.

In the worst cases you could administer bute (under your vet's supervision) for pain control in the first instance but, if you have a horse with a history of tying-up, it is far better to keep an herbal alternative on hand (see Chapter 4: Anti-inflammatories).

Bones and Connective Tissues

Horses – because of their design (a weighty body on relatively fine legs), their work (particularly horses partaking in rigorous performance sports), their propensity for rapid flight and the unnatural conditions in which we keep them – are prone to a great number of conditions and ailments of bones and connective tissues. Herbally, the treatments for many of these conditions are similar but we have divided the section into some of the more common complaints for the sake of easy reference.

Arthritis and Rheumatism

Arthritis is a diagnosis that is loosely used for any sort of physical change showing up in joints, or even for unidentified lameness. The orthodox prognosis is that this is somehow not the fault of the handling or treatment of the animal, it is just a fact of life; it may somehow resolve itself but most likely not. The recommended conventional treatment is with anti-inflammatory drugs like bute and perhaps calcium supplements. All of this and the sense of helplessness that goes along with it, is, of course, nonsense.

It is true that in old age a horse's structure (like ours) seems in many cases to stiffen up. It is also true that injury incurred earlier in life can accelerate the loss of mobility and result in pain due to the progression of a process started back with the original injury. But none of this is really inevitable in the way we are encouraged to believe.

Our bodies and those of our horses are designed to repair themselves as they go along. Every tissue cell, including those forming muscles, bones, ligaments and scar tissue, is replaced at regular intervals and there is no reason why this replacement process cannot lead toward resolution rather than toward progression of a structural problem.

Herbs have been used successfully for thousands of years in a hundred different cultures to treat all stages of all these problems loosely called 'arthritis'. An important ingredient in all such treatments was also a healthy dose of common sense and a good, hard, holistic look at an animal's history, diet and circumstances.

Any physical injury or process involving dense tissue – including ligaments, ligament attachment points, bones and scar tissue – is treated according to its state of progression. In a younger horse with a recent injury, free access to unimproved pastures and unrestricted exercise may be all that is required. In older horses with a history of stiffness and lameness, the approach will be different.

When approaching a problem of this nature it is necessary to distinguish between only two types of processes – arthritic and rheumatic – and this is the best way to set up a suitable treatment path.

Arthritic processes are those that involve changes in the structural components of the joints, which you would expect to show up on X-rays when they were further advanced. Rheumatic processes are to do with blood-chemistry problems, which translate into problems with the chemistry of the lubricant fluid in joints (synovial fluid).

Arthritic processes therefore require attention to the healing and nutritious herbs, the body's absorption and utilization of minerals and management of the balance between different minerals, which all work in harmony to normalize abnormal bone growth.

Rheumatic processes require attention to the systems in the body that regulate and normalize blood chemistry: often just the kidneys, but also perhaps the liver and the lymphatic system.

PREVENTION

In the first consideration, it is ridiculous to pretend that modern management and feeding of horses does not cause most of our 'arthritic' problems in the first place.

Concrete stable floors (in fact, restricting natural movement, exercise and stretching patterns by any sort of enclosure) are probably the primary reason for the structural fragility of the modern horse. This combined with the exposure to chemicals in feed, in the environment, in supplements and in injectables, further compromise the horse's health.

In this context, to say that arthritis is inevitable after an injury, or a natural result of old age, or that arthritis is a result of some sort of genetic weakness and can only be managed by painkillers, is absolutely incorrect.

Adopting more natural and chemical-free management programs is the best possible preventative measure for arthritis and related conditions. Basically, there is an incredible amount we can do with the application of a little common sense and a few simple herbs.

HELPFUL HERBS

In the case of an otherwise healthy young horse that has suffered an injury, an herbal mix is simply made to stimulate the healing process internally and provide exactly the correct nutrients for the complete rehabilitation of the injury.

This structural healing and rehabilitation mix is made from 4 kg each of freshly ground linseed and freshly ground white French birdseed millet, $\frac{1}{2}$ kg yarrow, and $\frac{1}{2}$ kg kelp. Prepare 2 liters of comfrey root extracted into organic cider vinegar, along with twenty drops of Bach Flower Rescue Remedy.

One cup twice a day of this mix is added to morning and night feeds along with 20 ml twice a day of the extract and continued for six weeks or more after the disappearance of the last of the symptoms or evidence of injury. One cup a day can be given as a maintenance dose.

Approaching this problem with an X-ray, a calcium supplement, bute, an operation and a rest when all else fails (which is a pretty normal progression), is basically useless and shows no understanding whatever of the processes involved.

Additionally, an external treatment, aimed at improving circulation within the particular area will speed up the body's ability to heal itself, while providing some relief from inflammation and helping to prevent excessive scar tissue formation – either internally or externally. The herbs involved in such treatment are 10 ml each of wintergreen, comfrey, arnica, rosemary and white willow bark extracts, and a tablespoon of kelp, added to 200 ml of linseed oil, applied to the area twice daily. Alternatively, the above oils and kelp can be added to arnica cream from the health-food shop to make a cream application. If too much swelling occurs with the external treatment you should reduce the amount of arnica in your mix, as this will be the problem.

The healing resulting from this type of treatment will be spectacular in the speed and resolution of the injury. It will require only six or eight weeks of treatment before you can bring the horse back into work with a rapid build-up to full workload.

At the other end of the scale, with an older horse experiencing rheumatic problems of stiffness and pain, regularly administered rosehips tea as a kidney and blood tonic is highly recommended. You can also make up herbal extracts containing bog bean, celery seed, dandelion root, white willow, yarrow and homeopathic ingredients to help manage tension and pain. These are best mixed and supplied by a professional herbalist.

This sort of treatment will encourage the reversal of the rheumatic processes, reduce inflammation and pain and result in a marked improvement in comfort and mobility.

In between these two extremes there are a combination of treatment approaches that may be used according to the type and severity of the horse's condition. In all these scenarios, avoid the use of phenylbutazone unless there is no alternative to short-term pain management. It is far better to use the natural alternative (see Chapter 4: Anti-inflammatories).

Ligament Problems and Bowed Tendons

Lameness, stiffness and soreness problems in horses are often the result of structural problems and ligament damage of one sort or another - whether it be recent or in the past. Sometimes these are related to, or occur in conjunction with bone problems (see Arthritis and Rheumatism on pages 160–161).

PREVENTION

Ligament problems are fairly difficult to prevent, as they are, more often than not, the result of accidents rather than the result of dietary or physical neglect. However, it is very simple to use herbs in the diet to ensure the maximum strength and elasticity in ligament development in horses, which will help to prevent many problems from occurring.

Bowed tendons in racehorses and pacers can be made less likely to occur and can be rehabilitated, if identified early enough, by the immediate application of tendon and bone treatments externally, with support from the seeds and herbs recommended below used internally.

HELPFUL HERBS

Internally

Add the following to the horse's daily rations.

Oats or millet: both contain especially high levels of organic silica compounds and, as oats can be too 'heating' for some horses, a daily half cup of freshly ground millet as a feed supplement is sufficient to ensure all the silica required to aid in recovery from injury.

Linseed is specific for strength and elasticity of ligaments and attachment points. A half a cup of freshly ground raw linseed daily is the herb to add into a program of treatment to speed up recovery and to promote strong and healthy healing of ligament injuries. It is also an excellent preventative in that it helps to keep the horse's connective tissues healthy.

Note Beware of the 'more is better' trap with linseed. Most herbs and seeds mentioned in this book are perfectly safe to feed in increased doses, not better than the prescribed doses, but safe; linseed is not. Small amounts of freshly ground linseed are fine, larger amounts are not and can be toxic, as the seeds contain traces of prussic acid, which is potentially toxic in large doses. Linseed can also be fed safely if the seeds are soaked and then boiled up to form a glutinous mass that can be mixed with molasses and given a cup at a time in the horse's feed. *Do not ever feed linseed oil internally*.

White willow bark is an herb containing natural salicylates and is a natural anti-inflammatory and painkiller. It is a useful ingredient in a bone and ligament treatment program, (10 ml of extract added to feed twice a day) as it reduces inflammation naturally and will reduce stiffness and soreness to allow a more even exercise program during recovery, without inappropriately masking pain. White willow is also a useful ingredient in a mixture to minimize stiffness and soreness in an older horse with a history of losing stiffness once he has warmed up.

Externally

A daily application of raw linseed oil to the legs of young horses is the very best thing to avoid a working life plagued by ligament injuries.

Wintergreen oil and arnica are applied topically (externally) twice a day, specifically to improve the circulation around healing and these are important in assisting the healing process in limb injuries. Both wintergreen and arnica are ingredients to include in healing creams and oils, but care must be taken not to use too much if you are making them yourself (50 ml of each to 500 ml of linseed oil, or base cream). Make sure also not to use them too close to fresh wounds because neither is antiseptic and in the early stage of injury they can slow the healing of an open wound. Wintergreen applied in an undiluted form can also cause the horse's skin to blister and arnica can cause spectacular swelling if used too freely on the lower limbs. Arnica should be used immediately on all bruising, especially on bone bruises to speed healing and to prevent the area from becoming the site for arthritic or even cancer problems in later years.

Yarrow is an herb which, in extract form, closes off blood vessels and acts as an astringent to help close up open wounds (see Chapter 4: Antiseptic/Styptic). Yarrow also stimulates bone-marrow health and the production of red blood cells within the bone marrow – again supporting the resolution, at the most profound levels, of damage or weakness to bones following strain or injury.

Comfrey is the most important herb in our repertoire in speeding up healing of structural injuries. Mashed up comfrey leaves mixed with linseed oil make a poultice (see Chapter 4: Poultices), that will astound you with the speed at which it will resolve ligament or bone injuries when used in conjunction with the other appropriate herbs above.

Navicular Disease

The diagnosis of navicular disease is often a death sentence for a horse and it is a condition that seems to have become more common over recent times. In many cases, it seems, 'navicular' is the tag given to lameness that defies specific diagnosis. Officially, navicular disease is characterized by changes to the navicular bone (which is situated under the frog, lying close to the pedal bone within the hoof), causing pain in the area, which makes the horse compensate by putting more weight on the toe. This can result in contracted heels. Symptoms sometimes seem to come and go.

As a first line of treatment, a good farrier with a firm understanding of a balanced hoof can reshape the horse's foot (over a period of time, depending on the initial shape) and apply custom-made shoes to make the condition simply go away. Also, allow your horse to exercise freely in the field and keep him off hard surfaces as much as possible while healing is occurring.

HELPFUL HERBS

There are also herbal remedies that will help with inflammation and damage to the internal tissues that have proved helpful in cases diagnosed as navicular disease.

Half a cup of millet in the horse's feed daily is a good internal remedy and a poultice of mashed up comfrey leaves in linseed oil (see Chapter 4: Poultices), together with arnica ointment (available from health-food stores) will be of great benefit in the early stages of dealing with the problem. First, smear the front hooves with a layer of arnica ointment and then apply and bandage the poultice, which can be left on for three or four days before changing.

Splints

'Splint' is the term used to describe a number of conditions that are characterized by a swelling in the area of the splint bones (which are small bones that lie either side of the cannon bone). The condition can be caused by trauma, working on hard surfaces, too strenuous exercise on young undeveloped bones, or poor conformation.

PREVENTION

The first consideration with splints is to avoid them! Do not subject young horses to rigorous exercise before their bones are developed and do not exercise and run horses on very hard surfaces (concrete stable floors should certainly be avoided).

If you catch the splint soon after it happens – particularly if it is the result of a trauma like a kick or an injury - herbal first aid can help alleviate the problem immediately.

The first aid for any trauma to the bone whether it is a hairline fracture or a bone bruise is to apply arnica cream and treat the horse with Bach Flower Rescue Remedy. Actually, it is sound practice to have both of these remedies on hand whenever you are working the horse because they work just as well for humans as for animals.

Arnica works by assisting in the flow of blood and fluids to and from the site of an injury, thus reducing bruising of soft tissue and bone. This greatly reduces the probability of a calcification occurring at the site of the injury and speeds up the healing process.

After a couple of days on arnica, a poultice of comfrey leaves mashed up in linseed oil and held on with a bandage will accelerate the healing of the splint by a factor of three, reducing recuperation and resting time from six to eight weeks to a mere three weeks. The poultice should be changed every two or three days. Kelp leaves can also be added to the poultice.

Comfrey taken internally, two or three young shoots, or one leaf in the horse's feed daily, and kelp taken internally (powder or granules: a teaspoonful in feed) can also help in healing.

Ground linseed and millet (half a cupful of each a day in feeds) are also helpful.

Shin Soreness

Horses subjected to hard work too young often suffer from shin soreness. The same remedies apply as for splints (see above).

Cuts, Abrasions and Wounds

Cuts, abrasions and wounds can be treated very effectively using natural alternatives to the usual application of commercial antiseptics and antibiotics. First aid should be the antiseptic/styptic formula (see Chapter 4: Herbal First Aid) and this should be followed by extra garlic, molasses and rosehips tea (see Chapter 2: Making Herbal Teas), which fed regularly will ensure that your horse's immune system is working well and is capable of dealing with any injury.

In the case of an injury, be sure there is no damage to tendons, ligaments etc. (if you cannot tell and the wound looks deep, seek professional advice) and give the horse Bach Flower Rescue Remedy (4–5 drops over the tongue).

Then, treat the wound as follows:

1. Hose the scratch or deeper wound well to dislodge any debris and put a few drops of an antiseptic/styptic mixture (which consists of extracts of yarrow, calendula and Bach Flower Rescue Remedy – see Chapter 4: Herbal First Aid) directly in the open wound. If the wound is gaping, pull the lips together with some sort of medi-strip or tape.

2. If there is associated swelling, apply arnica cream (from health-food stores) to the swelling but keep it away from the open wound.

3. Deep puncture wounds should be cleaned by applying a castor-oil poultice (see Chapter 4: Poultices) to draw out any infective agents or foreign bodies.

4. Give the horse echinacea and perhaps red clover internally, made up as a tea (see Chapter 2: Making Herbal Teas) but only if the wound becomes deeply infected and you are worried about the possibility of blood poisoning.

5. Do not over-treat. Let the horse's own immune system do its job with only an appropriate level of help.

Digestive System

Colic

Colic in horses is really just a description of pain in the gut. Any situation that stops the normal and relaxed functioning of the long tube forming the gastro-intestinal system can lead to colic. The tube can clog up and block with dried feces or other matter (impaction colic). It can partially block with sand (sand colic). There can be a stone blockage in the bile duct or somewhere in the urinary system causing pain and spasm (biliary or renal colic, which is uncommon in horses), or the tube can twist causing excruciating pain (life-threatening colic). Colic can also be the result of past worm damage in the intestine, or pain caused by migrating worm larvae.

Most commonly, colic can just be a temporary spasm caused by more gas than the particular part of the gut can handle easily. Sometimes parasites or infections are blamed but these factors are more likely to be a secondary rather than primary cause of colic. Digestive systems are dangerous places for 'bugs' when they are ingested with feed because the chemistry within the gut will destroy most of them on contact. Further, if the digestive system detects an organism, poison or mould that it does not think it can handle, the offending item is usually ejected through the mechanism of scouring (diarrhea).

As soon as there is any sort of blockage, problems result that cause severe pain. This is because the fermentation processes continue in the static material within the gut and gas builds up with nowhere to go. Pain itself causes muscular spasms in the gut, which makes the problem worse and the situation can get serious very quickly. The horse becomes stressed and this also exacerbates the problem. If he goes into shock, this in itself can be life-threatening.

First-aid advice is usually to keep the horse as comfortable and as quiet as possible during an attack of colic. If possible send someone else to do the running around and to phone the vet. As soon as you observe the symptoms – sweating, rolling, a dull expression in the eyes, the horse looking around at his sides, general agitation – take his vital signs so you can give proper information to the vet. Listen for gut sounds, check his heart rate and check the color of his gums (pale, bluish gums mean he has probably gone into shock and the situation is serious). If he wants to roll or seems agitated and keen to keep moving, it is best to keep him walking around; if he seems simply to want to stand still or to lie down quietly, let him find the most comfortable position.

In a non-surgical case of colic, antispasmodics and pain killers can assist while it all settles down and the veterinary variety of these drugs are much stronger and more fast-acting than the herbal ones. In a case requiring surgery to remove an impaction or operate on a twisted intestine, time is of the essence. Therefore, in an emergency, *get the vet quickly*, there is usually no substitute for medical intervention in these circumstances. However, do not accept antibiotics ("just in case") as all they will do is wreck the gut flora and this can lead to further complications.

PREVENTION

The best preventative or insurance against colic or a recurrence of colic, besides making sure of the quality of your feed, is regular exposure to chamomile tea. This, along with some rosehips, garlic, molasses and a cup of cider vinegar a day, are the best and simplest daily supplements to maintain general and digestive-system health in your equine friend (see Chapter 4; Natural Tonics).

If your horse lives in sandy surrounds, every six weeks or so give him a cup of psyllium husks (an excellent source of fiber that becomes a glutinous mass when ingested, helping to keep the gut active and to push sand through the horse's gut) in his feed every night for a week – but never during a colic episode, as it swells and can increase, or even cause, a blockage.

HELPFUL HERBS

Herbal first aid is, of course, an immediate dose of Bach Flower Rescue Remedy for the shock and reassurance, and be sure to take some of the Bach Flower Rescue Remedy yourself! While waiting for the vet to arrive, you can give the horse a drench of chamomile, dill and/or peppermint leaves made into a tea and fed at body temperature (see Chapter 2: Making Herbal Teas), if you can get him to take it; but remember that mad panic, rushing around and forcing something down a reluctant throat will probably simply aggravate the situation. A ginger and honey mixture (four teaspoons of ground ginger mixed into half a cup of honey) can also be helpful and a number of homeopathic remedies are considered effective in treating the different types of colic, e.g. nux vomica, aconite, colchicum and chamomilla. (See Reference section on homeopathic references for further reading.) 'Old timer' horsemen also swear that a bottle of body-temperature beer or stout can offer a horse relief from colic symptoms. (Again, it may be advisable to take some yourself!)

If you have to wait quite a while for the vet to come, administer your choice of the above herbal remedies every hour and continue to monitor the horse's vital signs.

The vet will be able to ascertain what is causing the colic and administer the appropriate emergency treatment.

It is after the acute episode has passed that the healing and recuperative powers of herbs come into play. Then, feed the horse chamomile and perhaps dill tea (see Chapter 2: Making Herbal Teas) and slippery elm paste (see Scours page 173). It is best not to feed hay or grain for at least twenty-four hours after the colic episode has passed but give the horse frequent small drinks of water, fresh green grass and bran mashes while everything settles down again.

Peritonitis

Peritonitis describes the inflammation, swelling and discomfort caused by infective or toxic material in the gut cavity, as opposed to within the gut itself. The problem can be caused by an injury that punctures the abdominal wall allowing foreign material to enter, or by the rupture of a cyst within the abdominal cavity. The other main cause of peritonitis is a puncture of some sort in the wall of the bowel, which allows waste material from the bowel itself to enter the gut cavity. The classic human equivalent causes are: a burst appendix; contamination by bowel contents following surgery; an infection within the abdominal cavity following surgery; a burst cyst; or following a reaction to an IUD etc.

Horses currently are subject to much less in the way of bowel surgery or other medical intrusion although, with the increasing popularity of laparascopic procedures, this may change. Presently, the most common ways for a horse to develop peritonitis are the spontaneous rupture of cysts, and infections resulting from puncture wounds through the abdominal wall – either by accident or following an emergency surgical procedure.

Treatment with antibiotics has always been the standard response and this often alleviates the symptoms of discomfort, lethargy and temperature. It never was the whole answer, however, because there is no easy mechanism by which waste products of infection could be cleared from the abdomen because it is a closed structure.

Nowadays, with the failure of antibiotics and the creation of resistant organisms, infections are difficult or impossible to control and peritonitis will become more and more common in humans and animals, as will complications following operations and injuries. We will rapidly be back to the bad old days of, "The operation was a success but the patient died of complications".

Cysts

The spontaneous rupture of cysts is an interesting biological mechanism. One of the capabilities of the immune system is the ability to identify and gather together toxic materials or the waste products of infection and package them up within a membrane to form a cyst, in order to isolate this dangerous material from the body. Cysts can occur anywhere in the body, but they are particularly valuable in closed structures like the abdomen where there is no easy way to discharge the waste material either into the blood, the lymph, the bowel, or to eject it through the skin.

The tendency to form cysts can often be a sign of some sort of inefficiency in toxin removal processes, especially if the cysts are close to the surface of the body and usually develop to the discharging stage. However, within closed structures like the abdominal cavity, the body's ability to form cysts is a life-saving process.

HELPFUL HERBS

Herbal treatments for peritonitis are relatively simple and revolve around herbs with natural antibiotic and alterative properties, the foremost of which is garlic, (yet another very good reason to train your horse to eat fresh garlic). Also beneficial are: colloidal silver; thuja; yarrow, rosehips, fenugreek and echinacea.

Thuja is used specifically for some of the exotic new infections – including Golden Staph – and is perfectly safe to give to horses.

Echinacea has been a very popular herb during the last few years and widely touted as an anti-infective, adopted by orthodox medicine and big business alike. In fact echinacea is not, on its own, an antibiotic at all. It is an alterative, in that it cleans the blood and it is the most valuable herb for clearing out residues of infections and other toxic materials from closed structures within the body. Most commonly these include an abscess in the root of a tooth or other bony structures and infection and inflammation in the abdominal cavity.

Then there is the herb red clover, another alterative. Red clover has a very specific property that makes it a requirement in any case of peritonitis: it is a specialist in thinning and breaking down the walls of cysts. This can have the effect of dumping a large and unexpected amount of toxic material into the bloodstream if it is taken by humans without supervision but, in the case of horses, the same cautions do not apply. However, it would be safest to allow your horse access to the fresh herb in the field, or only feed small quantities at a time: half a handful once a day is a good starting dose.

Treating peritonitis becomes a simple matter of feeding fresh garlic; rosehips and possibly fenugreek (as a lymphatic tonic) in herbal-tea form; and yarrow, echinacea and red clover as the dried herb (see Chapter 2: Preparing Herbs). If the peritonitis resulted from surgical intervention or followed unsuccessful antibiotic therapy, put the horse on a course of colloidal silver (20 ml internally twice a day) and include 10 ml twice daily of an extract of thuja in the treatment.

Scours

Scouring (diarrhea) is a fairly common problem among horses, most frequently in foals, young horses and racehorses. Often there are no other symptoms, and scouring in an otherwise healthy animal is usually evidence of a temporary disturbance in the horse's metabolic harmony. In such circumstances, the horse's liver becomes over-active – temporarily producing too much bile – frequently in response to a sudden influx of green feed, or as a result of contact from a fungal or other agent.

A progressive weakening of normal digestive balance due to an accumulating chemical load coming through the horse's feed, interruption in normal exercise patterns, or stress, could also cause this condition. Basically, the initial process of scouring is really the immune system at work attempting to clear any agents the body identifies as being harmful. Mostly, after the agent has been expelled, the horse's metabolism returns to normal.

Sometimes, however, the rushing of matter through the system sets up a pattern of irritation that remains after the cause has long gone, causing persistent scouring. When this occurs, the horse has consistently runny manure and is hard to keep in good condition. In such cases, the metabolic balance has remained disturbed and, often, horse owners will do a lot more damage using an increasing array of desperate measures and chemical medicines to solve the problem, creating an even greater imbalance in the digestive system. Expending effort in trying to identify and treat the original causal agent is usually a waste of time. What needs to be done in treating persistent scours is to deal with the pattern of irritation.

HELPFUL HERBS

The condition is characterized by an imbalance in the harmony of all the organs involved in the digestive process and an over-stimulation of the bowel wall, and herbs can be dramatically effective in restoring this balance.

The main herbs to use are extracts of dandelion root, chamomile flowers and fennel, to balance out the liver, the parasympathetic nervous system and the pancreas, respectively. These herbs may be made into a tea and either given to the horse as a daily drench (over the tongue) or added to his feed.

To make the tea, a couple of tablespoons each of dried dandelion root and fennel seeds and one third of a cup of chamomile flowers can be added to 1 liter of boiling water, and allowed to steep as it cools. This is poured over the horse's feed and mixed in – twice a day initially. As soon as the symptoms begin to subside, only give the tea once daily. It is also advisable to add a tablespoon of kelp to the horse's daily ration to support thyroid function.

Slippery elm bark powder is a very important and effective additional treatment for scours, in that it provides a soothing lining for the whole gut that allows the irritation of the gut lining to heal and settle. Slippery elm (available in powder form from health-food shops) is given at a dose rate of one third of a cup, with ten drops each of the Bach Flower Remedies impatiens and walnut, mixed into chamomile tea to make a paste and added to feed once a day.

Unlike the use of pharmaceutical chemical treatments, doses in herbal medicine are usually not critical at all; certainly this is the case with the herbs listed above. It does no harm to use relatively big doses at the beginning of treatment and then reduce the size of the dose as long as the frequency is consistent. The only exception to this is with a very young foal still primarily dependent on his mother's milk, when it is better to give large doses to the dam and very small ones to the young foal. When the horse's digestive system has matured and he is on adult feed, there is no bodyweight-type recommended dosage; what is important is that the horse has contact with the herb to allow rebalancing to take place.

As with all herbal treatments, for a full return to good health you must address the cause of the problem and continue the treatment for a period of time after the 'problem' has apparently gone away – remembering that the 'problem' is really only a symptom of imbalance! To ensure a full recovery, it is advisable to keep up the herbs to the horse for approximately four weeks after the symptoms have ceased. A complete course of slippery elm extends for a total of twelve weeks to allow time for the mucosa of the gut to recover completely.

Eye Conditions

As mentioned earlier, the prime province of the herbalist and herbal treatments is in the area of preventative treatment. With all acute conditions and traumas, it is advisable to have your equine health professional assess the horse before attempting to devise a course of action; it is then that you can decide which herbs to use as a primary or support treatment. This is particularly true of eye conditions, so if you are inexperienced in equine health care, have the condition diagnosed by a professional and then use the following information to select the appropriate herbal support.

Conjunctivitis and Other Eye Conditions

Eye conditions can occur as a result of foreign bodies (such as dust, chaff, etc.) lodging in the sensitive membrane lining the inside of the horse's eyelid (the conjunctiva) or as the result of an eye injury or infection. Such irritations can result in a condition called conjunctivitis.

The eye membrane of one or both eyes looks red and swollen and there is usually a discharge – either clear or pussy.

Another common eye condition in horses is an ulcerated cornea, which is when the surface of the eye has ruptured, usually as the result of an injury. The horse will have tears running down his face (usually only one eye unless he has suffered injury to both eyes) and be sensitive to direct sunlight. In good light, you should be able to see a tiny pit or abrasion on the surface of the eye that will appear bluish-white in color. Horses often present with this condition owing to the placement of their eyes on the head and the protruding nature of their eyes (which gives them extraordinary distance and peripheral vision),

The conventional treatment for most eye conditions in horses is the administration of antibiotic ointment or drops to the eye and, in some cases, atropine.

PREVENTION

Many of these injuries can be avoided: during fly season use fly veils on your horse as rubbing the head against objects to remove flies is a common cause, and hang hay nets below eye level because hay fragments are also often the cause.

HELPFUL HERBS

The treatment of many eye conditions can be simply and effectively carried out with the use of four herbal remedies.

The four remedies to use for treating all eye conditions are castor oil, celandine, golden seal and rue. Internationally renowned herbalist, Dorothy Hall, says that these four herbs are all that is ever needed to treat eye conditions in man or beast. Twenty years experience as a practicing herbalist has proven this to be true.

Castor oil, as has been noted in the first-aid section, is very effective in drawing out and removing debris from a wound. So, in the case of a foreign object lodged in the eye, Bach Flower Rescue Remedy should be administered directly into the eye (a few drops only) followed by a few drops of castor oil.

For infection prevention, this would be followed by treatment with the herbal extract mix of celandine, golden seal and rue, all in equal proportions. It is usually efficacious to add a few drops of the Bach Flower crab apple as well.

Golden seal is the key to this mixture and the early explorers to Central America apparently 'discovered' its properties. They noticed that while conjunctivitis was rife in the population of the time, the priests and others using a particular yellow dye around their eyes for ceremonial occasions did not have this sort of infection. The yellow color indicated a very concentrated form of vitamin E and it was found in the roots of the herb golden seal.

Celandine is an antiseptic and a further source of vitamin E.

Rue is a vascular tonic that improves the circulation thereby relieving the inflammation in the eye itself.

To alleviate all eye inflammations and cure most eye conditions, make an eyewash of the above ingredients.

Note The only caution in using this mixture is in its strength; the 1:1 commercial extract preparation of herbs is enormously strong and is to be used by adding a maximum of four drops of each ingredient to 20 ml of body-temperature water.

For horses the mix should be syringed into both eyes twice daily - a little at a time - for all cases of infection or irritation.

Recurrent Uveitis (Moon Blindness)

This serious condition is often the result of a depleted immune system, when an infection occurs inside the horse's eyeball. It often recurs after the initial onset and frequent recurrences or a severe episode when the infection cannot be brought under control can result in the loss of an eye. The condition can occur in one or both eyes. The affected eye will often cloud over, often eventually becoming sightless.

The horse will keep closing his eye/s against light and will have tears persistently running down his cheeks. A high degree of pain is associated with this condition.

Conventional treatment uses the injection of a long-acting corticosteroid under the conjunctiva and regular administration of antibiotic corticosteroid eye ointment.

By far the best approach to this, as well as the myriad other conditions resulting from a compromised immune system, is prevention. Follow the care regimen advocated in these pages and your horse will have the strongest possible immune system, which means that these sorts of problems simply will not occur.

HELPFUL HERBS

This is definitely not a condition that should be treated using just home remedies because it has a fast onset, is extremely painful and usually requires the health professional to bring in the 'heavy artillery'. Herbal treatments, however, can support and nourish the horse's immune system and help to minimize the effects of the drugs used to treat the condition. In addition, Bach Flower Rescue Remedy will help the horse with the shock of the extreme pain that characterizes moon blindness. Also, use the eye treatment for conjunctivitis in conjunction with pine bark and rosehips as an herbal tea (see Chapter 2: Making Herbal Teas) as support treatments to help boost the horse's immune system.

Hoof Conditions

Abscesses

Herbalists become quite excited by abscesses and other discharges of pus because they are a manifestation of the immune system at work.

With horses, abscesses most commonly occur in the hoof, although it is possible for an abscess or boil-like condition to occur anywhere on the body, or at the site of an injury.

Quite rightly the ancients assumed that pus and abscesses were a reflection of 'dirty blood' or a discharge of 'bad humors' and even as children we learned that pus was dead white (fighter) cells that have been doing battle with infection. Modern medicine has taken the attitude that an abscess is an infection and must be dealt with using antibiotics and that pus is the product of infection and therefore also calls for antibiotics. This is nonsense.

A robust immune system will very actively and positively discharge waste products of infection or inflammation. An immune system that is not quite so robust, or is otherwise busy, will often wrap up such products into little packages (cysts or abscesses) and tuck them away somewhere out of harm's way to be dealt with later.

Occasionally, after a bad bout of founder (laminitis), a puncture wound or a stone bruise, an abscess will form on the underside of the horse's hoof or around the coronet band and a discharge will occur. The reason for this is that circulation and available blood supply in the hoof and lower limb is so sparse it is not sufficient to carry all the by-products of injury or infection back up the leg. These are simply expelled through the sole of the hoof, through the coronet band, or even directly through a fissure that forms in the wall of the hoof itself. These processes are to be encouraged.

It is acceptable for the farrier to open up an abscess in the hoof to let it drain in order to hurry the process, although of course it will open on its own when it is ready.

However, it is not necessary, and indeed is often counter-productive, to give antibiotics 'to stop infection' if an abscess has matured and on the point of discharging itself. At this point, the whole immune system is poised to expel undesirable waste material and, while within the body of the waste there may be all manner of secondary 'bugs' feasting away, systemic or blood poisoning will not result from these products unless the process of discharge is inhibited.

It is, therefore, even more likely that more deep-seated problems will develop if interventionist measures are adopted. Antibiotics given to any animal with a ripening abscess, boil or cyst can serve to inhibit the natural discharge, as they can kill all this festering material that is actively assisting the immune system in breaking down tissue to form an opening to the surface.

HELPFUL HERBS

The two techniques used by herbalists to assist the body in clearing out waste products are the practice of applying poultices and other drawing agents, and the use of a class of herbs called alteratives.

Poultices are covered in detail in Chapter 4; suffice it to say here that there is no better drawing agent than castor oil. Every abscess or discharge should be encouraged by applying castor oil either directly to the opening, or mixing it in with a poultice carrier and taping or strapping the poultice in place. Please note, however, that there must be an opening through which to draw, so do not be impatient. Wait until an opening appears naturally; castor oil applied before an abscess has matured or where there is no opening to draw through will cause pain unnecessarily. (Castor oil is also to be included in your first-aid kit for drawing material out of puncture wounds to avoid these becoming sites of infection in the first place.)

Alteratives are all herbs that are particularly high in iron and sulfur and that work to support the blood in a variety of ways.

The three most commonly useful for abscesses are: garlic, red clover and echinacea.

Garlic is high in sulfur and is an antibiotic, an anti-infective and an alterative. Garlic can be used in a poultice also, but for blood-borne infections it is best given internally and fresh (see Chapter 4: Natural Tonics).

Red clover is one of the most powerful alteratives and is specific for the treatment of cysts. Red clover works by breaking down the walls of cysts so that the stored waste material can be released into the blood stream, so the effect is often the formation of a boil or discharge in a horse's hoof or lower limb (or indeed anywhere else). Red clover therefore could be seen to 'cause' abscesses but, of course, all it is really doing is stimulating a waste removal process that is to be encouraged and followed through to its conclusion.

Echinacea is very specific for the removal of the residues of deep-seated or past infections that remain in the blood or diffused through tissue - not packaged up as in the case of cysts. Echinacea is not a panacea for the whole immune system but it certainly will make you or your horse feel better if you have been running around half poisoned by your own blood!

Garlic should be given in larger doses when you are concerned that an injury or an infection could result in problems. Red clover should be encouraged in pasture and can be given in small amounts (a tablespoon of dried herb a day added to feed) to effect a gradual breakdown of any cysts that could have formed, even if they are not apparent on the surface. Echinacea could be fed fresh to your horse in season and in small amounts (a tablespoon a day) , just as a 'tune up', especially if your horse is an ex-racer with any sort of history of regular treatment with antibiotics.

Ideally, you could prepare any horse at risk by regularly feeding the above herbs in this way, so that if there were a major problem you would be able to use larger doses of these herbs confidently for a specific abscess, boil or cyst. All this would occur without running the risk of clearing out more than you had bargained for, too quickly.

Other herbs that assist alteratives for humans are those that are high in silica (like celery and equisetum), the purpose of which is to assist in driving material out by providing impetus to the formation of openings. However, dried feed like hay and chaff is very high in silica and, medicinally, it is not necessary to supply any more to horses. Perhaps the high silica diets of pasture-fed horses is the reason their systems often produce many more abscesses and discharges than we can with our modern diets that are very often far too low in silica.

Brittle Feet

Many horses suffer from brittle feet – often caused by incorrect feeding, stress, or poor hoof shape as a result of poor farriery. There are a multitude of expensive feed supplements and hoof preparations on the market that purport to improve hoof quality but, before rushing off to purchase any of these, consider what might be causing the problem in the first place and try some simple herbal remedies.

Where a horse's feet seem to be too brittle, or too soft, the first thing to address is the underlying cause. First, make sure he is receiving a balanced, simple diet that consists of the best quality, most unprocessed feed you can acquire. Adding rosehip tea, kelp, molasses and cider vinegar on a daily basis will help to keep his general health in top condition (see Chapter 4: Natural Tonics).

Stress can also cause hoof problems so, if this is a possible cause, look at your horse's lifestyle and consider using some nervous-system herbs to calm and destress him. Useful herbs for the various nervous-system types include vervain, valerian, hops, chamomile and passion flower (see Chapter 4: Nerve Tonics).

Then, look at the shape of the horse's feet; if they are too long in the toe or under-run in the heels, this can impair the integrity of the hoof wall, causing it to break down. If you suspect this is the case, ask your farrier to address the problem, or consider changing farriers.

PREVENTION

Regular application of a hoof-oil preparation can be used as a preventative, a healing agent and a general-purpose hoof-health tonic that also improves the circulation in the hoof. An excellent multi-purpose hoof oil can be made using the recipe in the following section on founder. The oil is then simply applied to the hoof walls and soles of the hoofs daily.

HELPFUL HERBS

Along with correcting the underlying cause, there are some herbs that can be very useful in restoring hoof quality. Rosehips, equisetum herbal tea (see Chapter 2: Preparing Herbal Teas), oaten hay, a little ground millet and linseed (half a cup of each twice a day), fresh comfrey leaves (one large leaf or a few shoots a day), are all helpful if fed to the horse in his daily rations.

Founder (Laminitis)

Founder (or laminitis) is a condition where the sensitive laminae that surround the pedal bone inside the horse's hoof become inflamed. This is usually a condition that only affects the front feet – although it does very occasionally occur in all four feet and can be very painful. Founder can be acute or chronic and, once a horse has suffered the condition, it is likely to recur. The conventional treatment usually involves the use of anti-inflammatory drugs until the inflammation subsides.

Over-indulgence on the lush green pastures of spring, eating excessive amounts of grain, drinking large amounts of cold water after exercise while still hot and heavy irregular exercise on hard surfaces are often blamed for outbreaks of founder in horses. Gut problems and pregnancy can also seem to result in founder and ponies seem to be especially prone to the condition.

From a holistic point of view, it is not really these various circumstances that need attention. More realistically we need to look at why some horses are susceptible and others are not and it seems likely that this is all to do with the circulatory system.

Equine hoof problems can be traced to the circulation in the lower limbs and hoofs. There is very little muscle tissue in the lower limbs and not a great deal of blood flow in the area. This is not surprising really because the lower limbs and hoof are mostly made up of bones and connective tissue of various sorts that do not require the massive blood flow needed by muscles. All the muscles that drive the leg are located up at the top, closer to the major blood vessels and the heart.

The 'designer' of the horse came up with this approach and it is very efficient for what the animal needs to do. However, like all special-purpose designs, there are problems:

*   The design of the equine limb and hoof means that the healing of an injury in the area is difficult and often slow, simply because there is not much blood available to nourish damaged cells.
*   Inflammation is difficult to dissipate because, again, there is little blood flow to carry it away.
*   Also, there is little spare blood capacity, so that sudden changes in circulation either in quality or quantity (what we could call circulatory shock) can affect the health of the hoof.

If you look at the design of the blood supply coming down and around the base of the pedal bone, you can visualize the pumping mechanism involved in moving blood around the hoof. When the weight comes onto the pedal bone it moves down slightly and compresses the blood vessels buried in the surrounding tissue. When the weight comes off, it releases the compression and the blood will flow. This is the pump.

As a first consideration, it is then obvious that what we as owners and our farriers do to the natural shape of the horse's foot will have consequences in terms of circulatory efficiency. If the hoof is undercut at the back, the tissues and the blood vessels are already stretched and compressed, which reduces the efficiency of the pump and of blood flow. This is why the health and management of the hoof is so important. Similarly, if a horse is confined on a hard surface with little room to move about for long periods of time the pump will not work efficiently.

Acute founder occurs initially as the result of a sudden circulatory shock and it most often seems to follow either an over-indulgence in lush spring feed or a sudden temperature change.

The lush feed overdose

In this case, and this is just a theory, a major exposure to fresh green feed (often clover) or an assault by the horse or pony on an open feed shed, can cause a sort of circulatory shock. This is more to do with blood chemistry than blood quantity. Let us assume, for example, that a sudden overdose of plant sugars – such as those found in fresh growth or seed – alters and perhaps temporarily slightly acidifies the blood. This could be sufficient to provide the chemical shock to the circulation that leaves it unable to nourish small areas of hoof tissue, which then begins to die.

In a horse's natural environment, devoid of human intervention, the horse's condition would change quite markedly within the seasons: being fat and round in late spring and summer and fairly lean and ribby by the end of winter before the fresh feed came in. Another potentially major factor in founder is the way in which we artificially keep condition on our horses right through winter, resulting in an overweight shock with the first of the spring feed. This causes an extra load on the hoof and subsequent circulatory shock.

We can also speculate that the susceptibility of ponies to founder can be related to their genetic origins as opposed to their current circumstances. Ponies evolved in high, poor country where they were never over-fed and had to work hard to find and graze sparse dry feed or even sparser fresh green pasture. In the winter they usually had to dig through the snow for feed. The modern pony is often a pet, frequently kept in pasture where in a good spring he can find himself standing up to his belly in clover. He is frequently also overweight, under-exercised and often bored. The same pony, being among the smartest and most persistent rogues of the equine world, will be the one to find a way into the bottom pasture or the crop, or to learn to slide the bolt on the feed shed door. All these factors predispose ponies to founder.

The sudden temperature change

During the change of season, a horse may be subjected to the extremes of hot ground underfoot during a hot spring day, followed by a frost at night; they often stand in an icy cold winter-temperature dam or creek on a hot spring day. In such cases a susceptible horse, whose circulation in the hoof is a little marginal anyway, can suffer an episode where the blood vessels contract suddenly under such conditions and temporarily reduce the circulation to a point where some tissue dies from under-nourishment.

Whether it is caused by the temperature or the chemical shock – or some other thing altogether – this is founder.

Following malnourishment of tissue and localized necrosis, the body sets up a pattern of inflammation and reabsorption, while in really bad cases the debris from the subsequent healing effort can sometimes be expelled through the coronet band or the sole of the hoof. There is a lot of pain and often structural changes if the pedal bones sink into the affected tissue and become permanently displaced.

Founder is, therefore, often characterized by this major structural damage, a long rehabilitation time and a predisposition to relapse that can remain for years afterward – if not permanently.

PREVENTION

Maintaining a natural, balanced hoof shape with short toes and heels that are not under-run will maintain healthy circulation in the hoof. A good farrier knows that hoof-shape management is critical for prevention of, and to aid in recovery from, founder, so get a *good* farrier and you may never have to deal with the condition. (See the section on References at the back of the book – *The Natural Horse* by Jaime Jackson provides excellent information on hoof shape and care.)

The release of pressure in an attack of founder is also important and some farriers make small nicks around the hoof to release this pressure and speed healing. Special shoes can also be fitted to relieve the pain of pressure.

Also, a horse with generally good health – a strong immune system and a healthy circulatory system – will be unlikely to suffer from founder, so follow the general health guidelines in the book to give your horse the best chance of avoiding this painful condition.

MANAGEMENT PRECAUTIONS

- Keep any susceptible horse off too much fresh green feed and keep the feed shed locked.
- Provide shade from the heat – particularly during the change of season from cold to hot.
- Provide warmer areas to shelter during cold snaps in the spring.
- If you must lock him up, provide accommodation that allows him plenty of room to move and flex, relief from the hard floor and room to lie down comfortably.
- Take care to minimize sudden exposure to icy cold water or conditions when there is no opportunity to exercise.
- Do not exercise the horse intermittently on hard surfaces.

HELPFUL HERBS

Any preventative measures that improve circulation in the limbs and especially the hoof will dramatically reduce the chance of founder. The same treatments will dramatically aid in the recovery of the condition.

Feed mixes can be given to the horse that contain all the nutritional requirements to heal damaged bones and connective tissue, while at the same time stimulating the circulation and the whole healing process. These are all those herbs and seeds discussed under the preceding sections on bone and connective tissue conditions. In addition, herbs that promote and protect peripheral circulation like rosehips, rue and maritime pine bark should be considered (see Chapter 2: Preparing Herbs).

Externally, a hoof-oil preparation can be used both as a preventative, a healing agent and a general-purpose hoof-health tonic, which also improves the circulation in the hoof. An excellent multi-purpose hoof oil can be made using a base of 250 ml of linseed oil (very good for hoofs anyway), containing 1.5 ml of arnica extract; 6 ml each of rosemary oil, wintergreen oil, white willow and equisetum extract; 15 ml of comfrey extract; 14 ml of kelp extract; and ten drops of Bach Flower Rescue Remedy – all of which combine to maximize health and healing in the hoof. The oil is applied to the whole hoof, the sole and around the coronet twice daily.

Note   Acupuncture and acupressure treatments have been well-documented as valuable therapeutic tools for treating laminitis, so, in recurring cases, seeking the help of a professional acupuncturist may prove beneficial.

Stone Bruises

Stone bruises to the horse's hoof occur in varying degrees and are fairly common. A severe stone bruise can be very debilitating and can form into an abscess. Often a stone bruise to the hoof occurs while the horse is turned out without the rider or owner being aware that it has even happened until it reveals itself later as an abscess but, if one occurs while you are riding, the herb arnica is absolutely wonderful for bruising if applied immediately after the injury.

HELPFUL HERBS

Arnica works by improving the circulation both to and from the injury. This applies not only to soft tissue bruises but also to hard tissue bruises, even those in solid bone. If you can get arnica ointment on really quickly after any bruising injury, a bruise will come up and will be gone within an hour. More importantly, bone bruises will heal completely and not become sites for arthritis or even cancer many years later.

Immediate application of an arnica ointment (from the health-food store) will work very well indeed on *all* soft tissue bruising and on the hoof itself, not just a stone bruise. Regular maintenance with the hoof-oil preparation (see the recipe for hoof oil in Chapter 10: Founder) will deal with the resolution of any bruising that goes unnoticed during day-to-day work. Correctly handled, this problem need never result in any lameness or other related problems in the future.

Respiratory System

Respiratory Infections

A horse with a healthy immune system can still be subject to the odd chest, sinus or throat infection caused by a viral or bacterial infestation, just like humans. If our immune systems were perfect this would not happen, but none of us is quite that perfect! What happens in the case of such an infection is that our immune system drops its guard temporarily because we have 'overdone it' through excessive physical demands or a chill – but it can also be the stress depletion of B-group vitamins. This catches the immune system by surprise and one of the waiting 'bugs' that are always looking for a host latches on. If the horse is healthy, the immune system quickly gets back on the job and it will simply have a three-day battle with the bug. Just like a human, the animal will have a temperature, a cough, be lethargic etc., then the immune system kills the bugs, wraps them up in phlegm and the horse coughs and snorts them out – end of episode.

In our modern world, however, there are complications to this picture, as described in the section on Exotic 'Bugs' (see page 197).

In the case of a simple respiratory infection, the best herbal defense is a chest and immunity mixture, which fortifies the horse against a brush with a viral or bacterial infection. While not strictly needed if your horse has a healthy immune system, this mixture does reinforce the system so it is better able to cope with a more exotic problem if ever it should come in contact with one. However, if your horse's immune system is depleted and he struggles for weeks to throw off a chest or a sinus problem, you need to place him on a program to boost the immune system, specifically in the chest and upper respiratory area.

The mix to prepare for this condition is quite complex but this is just because it needs to cover all aspects of the chest and upper respiratory system in one formulation. You can choose from among the different herbs and make something up yourself that is a little more specific if you wish, or just cover the whole lot in one hit.

HELPFUL HERBS

To make up the general chest and immunity tonic to keep on hand, extract the following dried herbs into enough organic cider vinegar to cover them, adding vinegar as the herbs swell (see Chapter 2: Vinegar-based Extracts):

- 150 g elecampane, as support for the muscular power of the lungs and to provide allantoin (a cell proliferant).
- 300 g fenugreek seed, as a source of vitamin A, as a tonic and

restorative to the mucous membranes, especially in the upper respiratory system, and as a lymphatic tonic.

- 300 g kelp, as a source of trace elements and mucilage to support the immune system, and to provide assistance with softening and soothing the linings within the airways.
- 150 g marshmallow, as a demulcent to soften and soothe irritations within the bronchi.
- 150 g mullein, which helps moderate the tickly irritations in the nasal passages.
- 150 g yarrow, as a high-iron herb, also to assist blood quality by supporting the red blood cell production, and as a central nervous-system tonic and astringent.
- 150 g nettle, as a major boost to the iron levels available to the blood to help with the oxidation of the infective agents.

Add to the mix:

- 1.5 kg fresh, peeled organic garlic cloves.
- 100 ml of maritime pine bark extract.
- 300 g of rosehips granules.
- 50 ml of an extract of coltsfoot (not essential but it will sometimes help as an expectorant).
- 100 g of thyme if the problem seems to be more localized in the throat than the bronchi or the sinuses.
- Ten drops each of the Bach Flower Remedies olive, hornbeam and wild rose – to deal with the feeling of depletion that accompanies a viral infection. These remedies are especially useful for any time when the horse's immunity has been lowered.

Allow the mix to steep for five or six weeks. Strain the herbs from the liquid – pressing the dregs to remove all the liquid – and add 10 ml of the resulting liquid twice a day to the horse's feed. Give the mixture for at least six weeks after the onset of symptoms.

In general management practice, give your horse rosehips tea regularly, as well as garlic (see Chapter 4: Natural Tonics) and, in the case of respiratory problems, it is helpful to add lemon to his drinking water. In the case of an outbreak of respiratory infections in your area, you can double up on the doses for all of the above to give your animals a better chance of missing out altogether on the outbreak. Remember also that organic cider vinegar is itself very helpful in fighting infection and you may choose to add a little more to your daily program at such times.

Allergic Rhinitis (Hay Fever)

Horses, like humans, often suffer from hay fever (or allergic rhinitis). This condition is characterized by the horse snuffling, sneezing and flicking the head, often with a runny nose that can develop into sores around the nostrils. These symptoms seem to occur most often in spring or summer, which suggests they may be dust- or pollen-related. Sometimes, however, a horse will present with the problem where there appears to be no distinct causal agent. The symptoms, while usually not in themselves serious, can be very distracting and disruptive for competition horses and generally cause some discomfort and distress.

It is important to understand that this condition is not really an illness in terms of a weakness in the immune system, but that it is rather an over-active or over-anxious immune system that is identifying a minor irritant and over-reacting to it. Coughing, sneezing and having your nose run is quite appropriate if the irritant is life-threatening, but the immune system should be able to recognize minor irritants as not dangerous and not react to them. Herbally, therefore, the approach to this condition is to nourish the immune and the nervous systems so that they are not over-reacting, then the symptoms simply go away. This is in direct contrast to the orthodox approach of prescribing antihistamines, a practice that ignores the underlying cause and simply temporarily suppresses the histamines in the body.

HELPFUL HERBS

The comprehensive list of herbs extracted into organic cider vinegar for treating allergic rhinitis has much in common with the herbs used for respiratory infections. Therefore we will only describe in detail the actions of those ingredients not common to both mixes here.

Garlic, fenugreek, kelp, mullein, nettle, pine bark, rosehips and yarrow all appear in the chest and immunity formulation on page 220 and are not further described here. The mixture also needs to contain:

- 100 g chamomile as support for the parasympathetic nervous system, which is involved in the over-enthusiastic immune system response underlying all allergic problems.
- 200 g euphorbia, which is very specific for the upper respiratory sneezing and snorting response.
- 1 kg of minced fresh horseradish, which in its fresh form is a wonderful support and tonic to the mucosa of the upper respiratory system as well as wonderful for clearing the blood of elevated histamine levels.
- 200 g vervain as the characteristic nervine applicable to the horse that tends to be overly sensitive to external stimuli.
- 1 kg fresh, peeled organic garlic cloves.
- 200 g fenugreek
- 200 g kelp
- 100 g marshmallow
- 100 g mullein
- 200 g nettle
- 100 g maritime pine bark
- 200 g rosehips
- 100 g yarrow
- Ten drops of the Bach Flower Remedies walnut for sensitivity and impatiens for the energy of over-reactivity.

Extract these into enough organic cider vinegar to cover them, adding vinegar as the herbs swell (see Chapter 2: Vinegar-based Extracts). Allow it to steep for five or six weeks, then strain the herbs from the liquid, pressing the dregs to remove all the liquid. Add 10 ml of the resulting liquid twice a day to the horse's feed.

As with other treatment programs in this book, the correct use of the allergic rhinitis formulation is for acute or current attacks, but be sure to continue the treatment for six weeks or so after all the symptoms have disappeared. Then, next season (if the problem seems to be seasonal), start the same treatment about six weeks before you would expect the condition to occur and watch your horse sail through the season with little or no problem. This herbal support releases the immune system from much depletion leaving it a great deal stronger to deal with more important issues.

Bleeders

'Bleeders' are those horses that suffer from exercise-induced pulmonary hemorrhage (EIPH) or bleeding from some part of the lungs. This condition can occur as a result of moderate to heavy exercise and is considered to be an athletic injury related to stress placed on the lungs by exertion. Many racehorses suffer the condition (although it can occur in any breed of horse, in any performance field). The condition varies in its severity, although the amount of blood loss is usually not significant, nor is the condition usually life-threatening. However, in severe cases, performance can be drastically impaired and for this reason repeat bleeders are banned from many types of competition.

There are those who say that all competition horses bleed from the lungs at some time during extreme exertion and this is probably true. Nowadays, quite a number of performance trainers are so paranoid about this possibility that they will 'scope' their charges (that is, have their vet look into the lungs with a endoscope) after almost every run. These trainers quite often have their worst fears confirmed and relinquish a steady stream of income continuing this practice. It is likely that it is not good for a horse to have a piece of equipment poking around in his lung cavity on a regular basis.

However, if it is true that all horses can bleed, then potentially all racers and pacers can be disqualified from any further competition if they are picked up with blood in the nostrils by the racing stewards more than twice, or whatever the ruling is in each different country. The difficulty faced by the industry is really the problem of distinguishing between a simple bleed (which can show in the horse's nostril after a race and has very little significance) and a severe bleed (which for all the correct and humane reasons should be cause for suspension).

Bleeding is the result of another one of these 'design problems', where the 'designer' is aiming for maximum efficiency, but in order to get this degree of efficiency has to go very close to the limit.

Horses' lungs are very large and powerful and they are driven by the gait during exertion. For example, as a racehorse draws his hindquarters forward at the gallop, he will pump the air very forcefully out of his lungs and will then draw it in just as efficiently when he stretches out. Of course, as he hits the ground each time his whole metabolic structure suffers a significant jarring. Added to this is the effect of turbulence, because the large mass of air being drawn in and then blown out forcefully creates a terrific amount of turbulence within the lungs and can produce localized areas of very high wind speeds – something like having a hurricane inside the lungs. All of this happens in an area of the body where the alveoli (the little blood filled sacs in the lungs) have a very fragile lining over them in order to allow oxygen to be drawn in directly through the lining (or the skin) covering them.

No wonder these horses often suffer from bleeding at some stage. What is amazing when you look at it like this, is that the 'designer' managed to make it work at all! Imagine being asked to design a bubble bath that will withstand hurricane force winds?

Pacers, since their gait is not a natural one for the speeds at which they are asked to perform, suffer more from bleeding because they do not have the benefit of the natural pumping action of the gallop. They are forced to take shorter sharper breaths and suffer more jarring to the lungs as a result of their pacing action.

Bleeding, then, is basically all tied up with the gait, the structural efficiency of the lungs themselves, the horse's fitness, the amount of scarring from previous bleeds and the strength of the lining of the alveoli. The best approach is prevention and herbal assistance to prevent a recurrence in the case of a horse that has already suffered a bleed.

HELPFUL HERBS

Herbally it is a simple matter to fine-tune the strength of the linings, which we do with a cup each daily of the herb rue and buckwheat. Rue is a most important herb in the treatment of bleeders because it strengthens capillary walls and increases capillary action and blood supply. Rue also helps to break up the venous congestion that often results from blood pressure changes. These are the two major components in the bleeding condition.

When a horse has suffered previous bleeds, there is the problem of the patch being stronger than the garment, i.e. the weakness along the boundary of the less elastic scarred tissue and the more elastic normal tissue is very often the site of the next bleed. It is also simple to improve the reabsorption and normalization of scarred tissue within the lungs to reduce the likelihood of this. This can be accomplished by using demulcent and healing herbs, especially comfrey (a fresh leaf in feed twice a day), which has both actions within the same herb.

Another useful approach to this condition combines a cup each of the dried herbs elecampane and marshmallow added to the horse's daily rations; elecampane improves the strength and efficiency of the lungs as a whole while containing allantoin as a healer, and marshmallow provides the demulcent action in soothing and softening damaged or scarred tissue within the lungs.

In herbal mixtures for bleeders, you can also include a daily dose of a cup each of hawthorn, nettle and yarrow, a tablespoon of kelp and 5–6 drops of Bach Flower Rescue Remedy. Hawthorn is particularly important for those cases where there has been a substantial and sudden bleed mid-flight, which virtually stops the animal in his tracks as the lungs partially fill with blood, rendering them unable to supply oxygen to the body. This situation produces an enormous shock to, and strain on, the heart: hawthorn and Bach Flower Rescue Remedy mitigate the effects of this sort of shock. Nettle and yarrow work at the level of blood quality, ensuring more efficient and healthy red blood cells and, as an astringent, yarrow can also assist in toning up the alveoli walls.

As a maintenance program for all performance horses at risk of this condition, they should have access to rue and hawthorn – either in their feed (one cup of each a day) or the hedgerow – and they should be fed a cup of buckwheat (which is the commercial source of rutin) daily in their diet. A mix containing most of the above herbs both protects racehorses against bleeds and also improves the efficiency of their lungs, allowing them to go faster.

Combining herbal treatments for bleeders with training and exercise programs – including perhaps gait modification and swimming – will help in restoring valuable performance horses to peak condition.

Equine Influenza

This condition is characterized by varying degrees of coughing and a runny nose, often leaving the horse debilitated and weak after the onset and sometimes beset by a persistent cough for months after the initial illness. Equine flu is the result of a viral infection; the symptoms can range from a mild case to being life-threatening and the condition should never be taken lightly.

The conventional treatment for equine flu is the administration of antibiotics (which are completely useless against a viral infection and are officially prescribed to combat secondary bacterial infections, which are rarely present) and sulfur drugs. Basically, orthodox veterinary medicine relies on a whole variety of treatments aimed at reducing the symptoms of illness, in the hope that the horse's immune system will fix itself, and antibiotics, which are no longer entirely efficacious or reliable because of abuse over the past forty years. There is also a considerable emphasis in many parts of the world on regularly vaccinating horses against equine influenza. Quite apart from the fact that this practice is known to cause side-effects in many animals and that the ability of the vaccine to prevent the condition is at best questionable, the very act of vaccinating the horse causes a grave shock to the immune system (see Chapter 4: Vaccinations and Injections).

By far the best approach to equine influenza is to build up the immunity in the lungs and the respiratory system and to clear residues from past and current infections. The immune system also needs to be boosted so it can deal with the viral infection itself and fight off any future infections. We also need to look at making the horse comfortable while the symptoms persist.

HELPFUL HERBS
Preventative

To give your horse the best possible chance of fighting off an infection, healthy immunity in the respiratory system is what you are aiming for and there are many old-fashioned remedies that can be simply incorporated into your routine.

Garlic is a natural antibiotic and selectively kills microbes that are not part of the normal group that inhabits the horse naturally (see Chapter

4: Natural Tonics). This is the major problem with chemical antibiotics because they do not discriminate and just wipe out all the 'bugs', some of which are very necessary for a healthy metabolism. They also then selectively promote resistant exotic bacteria and viruses with repeated use.

Rosehips are another great boost for the immune system. Cold rosehips tea at a rate of 1 liter a day can be added to molasses diluted in water and used to dampen down dry rations. The molasses itself is also good as a high natural source of sulfur and iron.

For a horse showing flu symptoms: add a sliced whole lemon to the drinking water; a tablespoon of the dried herb horehound in the horse's feed is good for a cough; eucalyptus oil is a great respiratory-system antiseptic (a few drops only added to feed); soaked fenugreek seeds (one cup a day in feed) are also very efficacious for upper respiratory problems.

Beyond the preventative measures, please refer to the complete description of the formulation for all respiratory-system infections and immune-system support. In a horse showing symptoms of a cold or flu, administration of the herbs should make a decided improvement in only two or three weeks. The important thing is to keep the treatment up for four to six weeks after all signs of problems have gone to ensure the horse's immunity is fully built up.

Equine Herpesvirus

There are a number of different herpesviruses that affect horses: EHV-1 that can cause fetal abortion (sub-type 1), which can also cause nervous disorders such as paralysis and hind limb incoordination, or respiratory problems (sub-type 2); EHV-3 causes blisters that can turn into deep ulcers on the reproductive organs of both mares and stallions.

All herpesviruses are amazingly adaptive, far more so than your average virus and bacterial infections and, although it is not really common knowledge, the equine herpesvirus (EHV–1) seems to be getting out of control. It is affecting a very significant proportion of horses – racing stock in particular – and it is showing up as respiratory symptoms.

There is a vaccine available that has proven to be ineffective and, as with human herpes, there are no medical 'cures' for the viruses. The spread and mutation of this virus is a direct result of the general depletion of the immune systems of our animals. We have created the circum-stances in which it can thrive simply by over-prescribing antibiotics and injections of all sorts and by using more and more chemicals on our land, in our feed and in the pollution of our water and air.

Unfortunately, the equine herpesvirus and other exotic infections are here to stay and will only be controlled by keeping our animals 110% healthy. No more quick fixes and magic medicines; we have used and abused these for fifty or sixty years and as a consequence we have seen the arrival of 'superbugs' and exotic viruses.

The only way to keep our stock free of this and other exotic infection is to build up and maintain the immune systems of our animals.

It will be the new strains of exotic infections that will be the biggest challenge to equine health over the next few years. It will be the complete failure of orthodox medicine to treat these exotics as well as its responsibility for creating an environment that created them in the first place, which will in all probability taint mankind's attitude toward twentieth century medicine forever.

HELPFUL HERBS

As a preventative measure, every day you need to feed your horses fresh garlic and rosehips in the form of an herbal tea (see Chapter 2: Making Herbal Teas). In the case of infection, support of the respiratory system by the use of herbal preparations including herbs like coltsfoot, elecampane, fenugreek, marshmallow, mullein, nettle and yarrow (see page 220). Colloidal silver (see Chapter 4: Antibiotics) and antioxidants like maritime pine bark extract (see Chapter 4: Antioxidants), are also indicated for equine herpesvirus, along with 5 ml daily of extract of thuja.

Additionally, minimize the use of medical drugs and injectables, stop using antibiotics where there is an alternative, keep away from veterinary hospitals where possible, and allow your animals access to clean natural pasture and supply them with hedgerows full of medicinal herbs and weeds so they may use their own instincts to self-medicate.

Exotic 'Bugs'

In Queensland, Australia, in 1995, a number of horses and their trainer died of an unidentified virus that, for the first time in recorded history, crossed the species barrier from horse to human. The whole Australian horse industry was identified as being at risk of annihilation from the virus (which caused severe respiratory problems) and panic ensued as horses from the one racing stable continued to drop. This also sparked a major health alert and scientists (as scientists do) worked frantically to figure out the origin of the virus and to classify it. Subsequently, another man who had been in contact with the affected horses died from the same virus a year later. There have been no other confirmed outbreaks of the virus, which is now tentatively believed to have come from flying foxes (a type of fruit bat) found in the area. The virus was labeled the equine morbillivirus and, later, the Hendra virus.

The real story behind this virus can be read in the comments on super-bugs in Chapter 4: Antibiotics. Whatever fine and learned conclusions the scientific community comes to, in all likelihood it will finally have been a result of over-use of chemical drugs. As with people, the competition horses' natural immunity has been savagely depleted in the last few decades by our abuse. In a natural environment the horses' instincts protect them from ingesting substances that can do them harm. Our response is to force-feed supplements and medicines over the tongue and, worse, to stick an arbitrary and dazzling array of exotic substances directly into the blood stream via needles.

HELPFUL HERBS

Simple common remedies like the following are deceptively powerful, will provide some protection for horses from whatever exotic 'bug' may arise by boosting their immune systems and should always be part of an equine health program.

Your horse should be fed garlic and molasses regularly; (see Chapter 4: Natural Tonics) and nettle and dandelion should be encouraged in the pasture or collected and offered regularly (a cup each of the dried herbs added to feed daily); nettle is extremely high in iron and is a major blood tonic, while dandelion detoxifies the liver. All stabled horses subjected to supplements and chemicalized feed need help in this area.

Other helpful herbs for any respiratory condition are listed throughout this chapter.

Roaring

'Roaring' is a condition that seems to be common among racehorses and is caused by a partial paralysis of the horse's larynx. The symptoms are a roaring or whistling noise made by the horse as he breathes in and these symptoms are usually only noticeable when the horse is exercising hard. Roaring diminishes a horse's ability to perform at his best and the conventional treatment is to surgically secure the paralyzed part of the larynx in its normal position: a procedure called Hobday's operation.

HELPFUL HERBS

This condition responds well to a combination of mineral supplements – especially dolomite – and herbs that are aimed at completely rehabilitating the lungs and the bronchial tubes (the same sorts of herbs were used for treating tuberculosis in the old days and are used for treating asthma and weak chests nowadays). After ascertaining that the chest and bronchial tubes are completely healthy (see Respiratory Infections on pages 187–192), the next focus is to administer herbs that work on the soft tissue and mucous membranes in the throat, nose and palate. These will be astringent tonics to tone and strengthen these tissues.

Long-standing severe roaring must cause stretching and damage to the soft tissue involved and it is probably not possible to bring these cases completely back on herbs alone. In such cases, herbal treatments in support of an operation and the healing afterwards might offer a better alternative.

Astringent tonics placed in contact with the affected area are the primary requirement. A paste made of a quarter of a cup of slippery elm bark powder mixed with a cup of cold yarrow tea and given over the tongue in several small doses once a day would be the primary treatment.

Also, train the horse to take lemons as a treat. This would best be done by adding slices of fresh lemons to all his drinking water and watch for him to begin to chew the slices themselves – after which he may take lemon directly from the hand. Lemon is a very strong astringent tonic to the mucous membranes within the bronchi, the throat and upper respiratory system, as is vinegar.

Skin Conditions

Fungal and Parasitic Infections

Dermatophilus and other similar skin conditions are becoming increasingly common among horses. There many possible underlying factors that initiate these conditions – insect bites, fungal and bacterial infections from scratches, etc. – and these are often cited as the problem, but the first thing to remember is that skin problems come from the inside.

Horses' skin, although sensitive, is reasonably well protected. If we do not wash out the natural oils too frequently, or feed too many strange and unnatural foods and chemicals and if we do not stress our horses too much, the skin will remain healthy. Any bites, injuries and scrapes will quickly heal and disappear on their own. However, it is a fact that skin conditions seem to be becoming more common and that they are often difficult to treat. This is most probably because we are weakening the skin's natural defenses – either by stripping natural oils with our shampoos, or by exposing the animals to more and more chemicals internally, which can have the same effect. The resultant chronic condition can range from localized itching and swelling, to hair loss, or oozing sores, and many horses suffer the same condition during the same season year after year.

Skin conditions have a variety of names and many do have their origins in overly sensitive reactions to insect bites or are the result of the horse scratching or rubbing himself for whatever reason. The chronic problem, however, develops because damaged or rubbed skin from the initial cause is very prone to fungal or parasitic infections and these infestations end up getting the blame for causing the problem. Mostly they are not the cause of the problem, rather they are simply parasitic and doing what parasites do best: taking advantage of a weakened host.

There are many different types of fungal and parasitic infestation but, whatever the specific fungi or parasites exacerbating the problem, there are really four aspects to look at, all of which must be considered together when dealing with these skin 'conditions'.

- Internal treatment to strengthen the horse's nervous system, which is probably of the vervain or the hypericum type.

- Internal treatment to boost the horse's immune system, liver, blood quality and general health – all of which are often involved in the over-reactivity.
- Physical or environmental protection against 'trigger' events or irritations.
- External treatment to soothe and heal the skin while discouraging secondary parasitic infestation.

PREVENTION

If you can prevent the horse from being bitten by whichever insect sets off the initial problem, you will make a start on treating the condition (see Biting Insects on page 204).

Since skin conditions are usually a reflection of an internal imbalance, make sure your horsekeeping practices are as natural as possible. In particular, wherever feasible avoid feed that is high in chemical residues and avoid unnatural feed supplements because these all add to the load on the horse's metabolism in general and the liver in particular.

HELPFUL HERBS

External treatments

The vast majority of horse owners use cortisone-type treatments externally to treat skin irritations and fungal infections. These weaken the skin and should only ever be used as a last resort in an absolute emergency. They should never be used long-term. Oily treatments should also not be used, as often grease protects and nourishes parasites.

Far more effective are preparations made up of diluted lemon juice or vinegar (100 ml), as they discourage fungal infections and tone up the skin and such preparations should include antiseptics like eucalyptus or thyme oil (5 ml) and garlic (3–4 cloves peeled and crushed) as an antibiotic. Thuja is a topical antifungal and can be obtained in extract form to include in a spray mix in small amounts (5 ml).

Good results in chronic skin irritations are often obtained by spraying or rubbing on colloidal silver externally – sometimes with a few drops of thuja added. Interestingly, this particular remedy is proving to be very successful against the Golden Staph infections now endemic in our hospitals, and it is only a matter of a short time before our veterinary hospitals and practices will be similarly infested.

To treat the sensitivity of the skin directly, massage a little hypericum oil into affected patches, or add 5 ml of hypericum oil to an herbal hair conditioner that has vitamin E or aloes in it, and massage that in before lightly rinsing.

Otherwise you can make up chamomile tea (see Chapter 2: Making Herbal Teas) using dried chamomile flowers or chamomile tea bags, and spray this onto a damp coat. The chamomile is then drawn down the hairs and ends up on the skin to soothe it. It is also possible to add hypericum oil to a spray bottle of chamomile by agitating it frequently and spraying. When you make up the chamomile tea, add any leftover tea and the dregs to your horse's feed.

For immediate relief, the common fresh herb chickweed can be crushed in the hand and rubbed into itchy areas, or boiled in lanolin and made into a cream.

On hairless patches, it is often difficult to encourage the hair to grow back because the parasites actually damage the hair follicles but, once the initial inflammation has subsided, comfrey ointment (from the health-food store) or rosemary oil massaged once or twice a day into the affected area can expedite hair regrowth.

Internal Treatments

A reaction on the skin is always a reflection of an internal lack of vitality because a healthy metabolism is designed to resist infections and infestations. Feeding a balanced natural diet will help create a healthy immune system, and the addition of rosehips tea, garlic and molasses to the diet will be of benefit (see Chapter 4: Natural Tonics). garlic also has the advantage of having antiparasitic properties that will assist in both discouraging biting insects and expelling parasites.

Herbs that are high in iron (like nettle) and liver tonics (like dandelion) will make a huge difference to the horse's circulation and blood quality, which is probably the major factor in a susceptible horse. Boil up 1–2 cups of nettle (dried or fresh) in 1 l of water and when it has cooled add this to the horse's drinking water; and either offer a few leaves of dandelion daily, allow the horse to forage where dandelions are plentiful, or prepare dandelion-root tea for him. Tea made from the seeds of the St Mary's thistle is another option for liver support (see Chapter 2: Making Herbal Teas).

Alteratives high in iron and other heavy minerals work to clear the blood of toxins, which can predispose a horse to skin reactions or infective conditions. Often an internal support mix will contain alterative ingredients such as echinacea, fenugreek, liquorice, red clover and violet leaves, for example, to clear and drive toxins from the blood, thereby reducing the horse's sensitivity to external irritants and improving skin health. This kind of specialized mix should be made up by a professional herbalist.

Immune-system support herbs – especially maritime pine bark and rosehips – can often be helpful if the horse's immune system was initially run down (which predisposed it to an overly reactive response) or was depleted because of prolonged itching and distress (see Chapter 4: Natural Tonics).

Greasy Heel/Rain Scald

Both greasy heel and rain scald are caused by the same bacteria and both are usually associated with horses living in wet conditions.

Greasy heel (dermatophilosis) is an inflammation of the skin on the back of the horse's pastern – just above and between the heels – the result of infection. It appears as a red, raw inflammation to begin with that is painful to the touch. As the condition progresses, deep cracks can appear, with hair loss and tough, thickened skin either side of the cracks. The condition is often caused by horses kept for long periods in wet or muddy conditions, may be the result of an abrasion or rope burn that allows the bacteria to enter, or can even be caused by too frequent washing with soap and water.

Rain scald is an infection by the same bacteria but this time the lesions appear on the horse's back, belly or lower limbs. In these cases the horse's hair mats and the area oozes liquid. Underneath the hair, there can be a raw bleeding surface. This condition is usually associated with horses that are left out in wet conditions for prolonged periods without shelter.

PREVENTION

Protection, i.e. providing horses with shelter from the elements (it does not need to be 5-star accommodation: a simple shelter belt of trees in the pasture will suffice) and making sure they have somewhere dry to stand in wet weather, is the first line of defense from these conditions.

If a horse develops rain scald or greasy heel, keep the affected area clean and dry.

HELPFUL HERBS

For any horse suffering from greasy heel or rain scald, follow the regimen outlined for Fungal and Parasitic infections on page 200. For cases of greasy heel, it is also advisable to apply the hoof-oil mixture (see page 186 in Founder section for the recipe) to the horse's feet twice a day. Where there is broken skin or raw areas, avoid rubbing the hoof oil into those areas and instead apply antiseptic/styptic (see Chapter 4: Herbal First Aid), or thuja ointment (available from health-food stores). Continue the application of the treatment for at least six weeks after the condition has cleared up; you might even want to consider using the hoof oil once or twice a week on a permanent basis.

Biting Insects

Biting insects, apart from the sheer nuisance value of fly and insect bites to the horse's comfort, can cause quite severe reactions, setting up a chain of events that can become a major health issue. Localized swelling and persistent itching are not uncommon reactions in sensitive horses and, sometimes, hard fibrous lumps that take some time to disappear from the site of the bite.

If the itch is severe enough, the horse may rub himself raw, leaving damaged and weakened skin that attracts fungal infections and other parasites (see Fungal and Parasitic Infections on page 200).

PREVENTION

As a first line of defense, try keeping a light cotton or shade-cloth type rug and neck rug on your horse during 'biting season'. In areas where biting insects are severe, fly 'boots' that cover the leg are also an option.

Clean manure out of pastures and yards, cover manure and

compost heaps to discourage flies from breeding and plant insect repellent plants around horse yards and stables (garlic, tansy, citronella-scented geraniums, lavender, rue and wormwood, for example).

HELPFUL HERBS

Citronella oil (available from health-food stores) is the best topical preparation to discourage biting insects. Mix about twenty drops of oil in a 500 ml spray bottle of water, shake well and apply to the horse in a fine mist. Like all repellents, it will not last long on a horse that is sweating, so needs to be applied frequently when the horse is being exercised and at least twice a day on a horse at rest.

Aloe vera is also very effective in relieving itches and stinging bites. Simply cut open a piece of the cactus (aloe vera is a hardy plant that grows in most climates) and rub the gel on the affected area. Pure aloe vera gel is also available from health-food stores. Dock leaves are acidic and will neutralize alkaline stings such as that of the wasp just crush a fresh leaf in your hand and rub on the bite. Bee stings on the other hand are acidic and are relieved by alkaline substances like bicarbonate of soda. Otherwise, lavender oil will be helpful.

Similarly, chamomile tea can be sponged or sprayed over bites to soothe the skin (see further comments under Skin Conditions).

Anhydrosis (The 'Puffs')

Although not specifically a skin condition, this ailment is where the horse is unable to sweat in extreme heat and humidity and therefore cannot handle a normal working program. It is usually a condition that occurs in tropical climates, particularly if the horse is moved from a cooler climate to a tropical one. However, exactly the same inability to sweat can manifest in temperate weather where it may be less obvious and even remain undiscovered if the animal is not worked hard.

A horse's fluid and electrolyte balance and his ability to cool through the evaporation of sweat are critical. It is a lot to ask that he adjusts from either cold/dry or hot/dry weather to hot/humid overnight. In the first instance, if you are moving a horse between extremes, give him time to acclimatize, or move him during the winter rather than in the heat of summer.

Also, if the horse has been on commercial electrolytes, take him off them long before he is moved in order to get his kidneys back to working properly so he can cope with the extra demand in the tropical climate. Then put him back on commercial electrolytes and extra salt when he first arrives and then wean him off them again, going back to the natural 'electrolytes' (see Chapter 4: Electrolytes). If commercial electrolytes are used judiciously in special cases like this and not given as a routine, all horses would be better off.

HELPFUL HERBS

The herbs that stimulate the lymphatic system and the sweat glands are fenugreek and equisetum (horsetail). Make up two cups of each into a tea (see Chapter 2: Making Herbal Teas) to be added to the horse's drinking water twice a day and do this for six weeks before moving if there are any suspicions whatsoever about the horse's ability to sweat freely. Continue the treatment for a further month in the new environment. Preparing mint tea for your horse and having mint growing alongside the water trough is another useful diaphoretic tonic that promotes sweating.

Keep kelp and sea salt freely available to the horse (see Chapter 4: Electrolytes) and give rosehips as part of his regular feeding regimen.

Sarcoids

A sarcoid is a type of skin tumor, thought to be caused in horses by a viral infection. Usually these tumors occur on the horse's head, legs or shoulders and somewhat resemble a wart in appearance. These tumors can vary in size, from tiny pin-heads to large golf-ball sized growths, and can have a thick crusty surface or a raw fleshy surface that bleeds easily. More than one can appear at the same time. Unlike other tumors, sarcoids are not known to metastasize to internal organs, but they can be quite fast-growing and can interfere with ligaments and tendons in susceptible areas.

The usual treatment for a sarcoid is to freeze it off or to surgically remove it.

HELPFUL HERBS

The herbal approach to a sarcoid treats the imbalance in the body systems that cause the condition in the first place. A sarcoid can be seen as an attempt by the immune system to 'package up' and expel something it perceives as harmful to the horse: for example, impurities within the blood, or the waste products following a clash with an infection. Therefore, the herbs to include in a mixture aimed at resolving the problem and facilitating the expulsion of the offending matter are as follows: echinacea, equisetum (horsetail), and mistletoe (as three of the most powerful and specific blood cleansers); comfrey (to support the immune system and assist the equisetum in healing any damage to ligaments etc. caused by the presence of the sarcoid); violet leaves (as a lymphatic tonic to further facilitate the cleansing via the lymphatic system); and vervain (as a nervous-system tonic supporting the whole process).

Note These herbs are best given in concentrated extract form and should be made up by an herbalist with access to such extracts. The horse's whole history must be taken into account when prescribing mistletoe and violet leaves because it is possible to make your horse ill if these are prescribed inappropriately.

Warts

Warts afflict horses quite frequently – usually foals and young horses up to three years old. They normally occur around the nose, cheeks, lips or eyelids and can vary in number from a single wart to a crop of literally hundreds. Often these will disappear of their own accord after a few months but they can be a very disfiguring condition for the show horse while they are in evidence. Horses are also inclined to rub the warts, causing them to bleed and leaving the area open to fungal and other sorts of infection and fly strike.

As this condition can be transmitted from one horse to another, make sure you clean tack, rugs and grooming equipment thoroughly before using on other horses.

HELPFUL HERBS

The most effective treatment for warts is thuja. Use in the concentrated extract form, dabbing directly on the warts once a day. Also, use insect repellent herbs externally (see Biting Insects on page 204).

Stringhalt

Stringhalt is a condition affecting the horse's hind limb/s. When the horse is moving, one or both legs are raised with an uncontrolled, jerky motion with the leg almost appearing to flick up against the horse's abdomen.

This is a most frustrating condition for horse owners. Various 'weeds' like dandelion and fireweed are blamed, but it is likely that there is some common fungus or other pathogen that inhabits these plants at certain times, which is responsible for the physical damage to the central nervous system of susceptible horses.

Treatments revolve around the herbs that physically rehabilitate the damaged central nervous system and the brain. The aim of the treatment is to clear the fungal or other exotic pathogen from the system and speed the horse's recovery, which often occurs over time – even in untreated cases. Treatments should also be formulated to help rebuild any muscle wastage resulting from the condition and to reduce the sensitivity, so that the horse will be much less likely to suffer from stringhalt again.

A fresh comfrey leaf and a tablespoon of sage a day added to feed provide the vitamin B12 and cerebro-circulatory support helpful in all cases of physical brain damage. Valerian and mugwort made up as herbal teas (see Chapter 2: Making Herbal Teas) are useful to administer to deal with damage to the physical nerve fibers, as both are high in magnesium phosphate. Also included are: saw palmetto, which is helpful in rebuilding wasted muscle tissue affected by nerve damage or inactivity, and maritime pine bark in case there is some benefit to be obtained from support by strong antioxidants. A professional herbalist should make up this herbal formulation for the individual horse.

The Bach Flower Remedies and homeopathic remedies to give the horse are: heather, elm, vervain, sweet chestnut, mag phos and pot chlor – 5–6 drops of each daily.

Adding a cup of acidophilus yogurt (from your health-food store) twice a day and up to a cup of dolomite to the horse's feed, along with the herbal formulation, have proved to be helpful.

Tetanus

Tetanus is a condition about which most horse owners have a firm understanding. The need for regular vaccinations for both horse and owner has been stressed for many years and there is no doubt that the incidence of this fast moving, potentially fatal disease has diminished markedly. There are problems with regular routine vaccinations, however, so while it is certainly not recommended to refuse to vaccinate your horse against tetanus, there are ways to minimize potential side-effects using herbs and homeopathic remedies (see Chapter 4: Vaccinations and Injections).

Tetanus is a form of poisoning produced by the bacterium *Clostridium tetani*. The bacteria live in the gut of many species – including horses and humans – and are passed into the environment via their feces. Because horses live to some degree surrounded by their manure, they are at high risk from infection. The bacteria produce spores that live in the manure and soil and, when suitable conditions arise, these spores grow into the tetanus bacteria. Deep flesh wounds and puncture wounds create exactly the environment the bacteria need in which to develop.

The poisoning from the bacteria causes neurological symptoms including muscle rigidity and spasms, the closing of the third eyelid over the eye, difficulty moving the mouth and jaw, drooling and, eventually, violent convulsions that frequently lead to death. The horse will also be very sensitive to light and noise, exposure to which may cause convulsions.

Horses are routinely vaccinated against tetanus every year with tetanus toxoid vaccine and given a shot of tetanus antitoxin in the case of a wound or injury to provide fast-acting protection. There is no doubt that this vaccination regimen saves lives in a disease that has upwards of a 70% fatality rate. However, vaccinating the horse every year after the initial protection (two shots, three months apart), is probably not necessary. Vaccinations every 3–5 years and using a tetanus antitoxin when the horse suffered any wound that could harbor tetanus would be a healthier option. Herbs and homeopathic remedies administered at the time of any suspect injury and maintaining a strong immune system will also assist.

Fast, effective treatment of any wound is a good preventative measure. The administration of an antiseptic/styptic mix (see Chapter 4: Antiseptic/ Styptic) to any wound will disinfect and aid healing, and poulticing puncture wounds with a pad soaked in castor oil or dropping castor oil into a wound will help to draw out any debris or infective material. The homeopathic remedies ledum (marsh-tea) and hypericum taken internally are reputed to be helpful in preventing tetanus, and a homeopathic preparation known as a nosode made from tissue infected with tetanus (tetanus nosode) is useful in both the prevention and cure of the disease.

Recovery, Recuperation and Radiance

Because herbs operate on every level of the horse's being and support all the bodily systems, they have a great deal to offer the horse owner at every level of care, from your day-to-day health care regimen, to every level of illness and debility. This section provides a useful guide to the several levels of herbal treatment available for degrees of debility, from the most severe (a life-threatening condition), to the least severe (a dull coat). It also provides a glimpse into the thought processes a professional herbalist might apply to decide on which of the herbs to provide for different degrees of debility.

Terminally Severe Debility?

At the level of the maximum debilitation, there is a time in a severe illness pattern or trauma when one must decide if there is any recovery available. This is not the time to load up the horse with an expensive array of herbal treatment. It is also certainly not the time for hospital emergency-room-type treatments like emergency injections, IV drips, transfusions or ventilation, which are phenomenally expensive and can only further shock the whole immunity and the very being of the horse.

Sometimes there is simply a point where you need to let the horse go: do not condemn him to poor life quality henceforth just to satisfy your own well-meaning but inappropriate inability to let go. There is possibly a case for using adrenaline for shock or for sedation in cases of very severe pain while you decide the best path.

Deciding the best path of action is often a difficult thing for a horse owner faced with a severely debilitated horse, particularly when emotions run high and hope tends to over-ride common sense. There is a very simple, old and cheap test to determine whether there is enough energy left in the being of the horse to pull out of severe debility. This is in the use of a vinegar-based extract of hawthorn berries or leaves and rosehips, to which has been added two drops of Bach Flower Rescue Remedy stock.

In an ideal world, it is this mixture the animal welfare agents should always carry for their encounters with abused and neglected horses; stewards and vets at the racecourse should have it on hand; and the attendants at the vetting points in endurance rides should hold it in reserve. This mixture is also what should be held at veterinary hospitals' reception areas, horse trials, jumping events and rodeos: anywhere there is a potential to encounter severe trauma or debilitation in horses.

What is required is a drench of a small amount of this extract (40–50 ml over the tongue), followed after ten minutes by another similar drench. If this simple treatment does not produce positive signs of recovery within another short period – a lifting of the head, a positive glance, some spark of life - say goodbye to the horse then and there because there is really no reasonable hope of recovery.

This might appear to be rather extraordinary advice; this extract seems to be too cheap and 'low tech', when at this stage of illness the medical industry would often be inclined to become very interventionist (and expensive), often suggesting more tests, more drugs, surgery. However, if you appreciate the power of the hawthorn and rosehips mix given to a horse in this condition, you will understand how decisive the test is.

In extremis, the hawthorn/rosehips extract works at two levels: both the physical and the energetic. It is a heart tonic in the sense that it provides an instant support to the heart muscle and the energy of the heart, helping it to recover from profound shock, which has always occurred by the time the horse has reached this point. Rosehips provide an almost instantaneous physical energy boost of vitamin C to the adrenal system, along with iron for the blood oxygen levels in the body. Bach Flower Rescue Remedy neutralizes the component energies of shock, specifically: vulnerability, fear, panic, loss of control and temporary paralysis of the central nervous system or core energy.

A response resulting from two closely spaced drenches of this mix gives a highly sophisticated and definite answer to the question the carer must ask at this point, "Can this horse recover from here?"

Severe Debility

Any horse that has suffered a severe trauma – accident or operation – or any horse that has been seriously ill for any reason can benefit from the judicious use of herbs. Far from disturbing or negating conventional veterinary treatment, herbs can be given alongside such treatments to expedite healing, to rebalance and support the immune system and to minimize the harmful effect of pharmaceutical drugs and surgical procedures. They can also often stand alone, particularly in the cases of metabolic damage like poisoning, neglect or starvation, for example.

The following herbal preparation has time and again had a remarkable effect in aiding a debilitated or recuperating horse and it is the one to have made up as an emergency 'bring-'em-back-from-the-dead' formula. The mix is carefully formulated to bring back normal functioning and to rebalance a metabolism thrown completely out by injury, illness or poisoning. It will often rescue a horse within days of death – as long as he can still be persuaded to eat and has responded to the 'terminal or otherwise' test, which is always the first-aid treatment in such cases.

The dried herbs in the mixture are as follows and they are mixed together in roughly equal volumes: ten cups each of borage, chamomile, dandelion leaf and nettle. To these are added four cups each of kelp granules and fennel seeds. After mixing, this dried mixture is dampened down with 500 ml each of vinegar-based extracts of dandelion root, garlic and hawthorn berries, to which twenty drops of Bach Flower Rescue Remedy have been added. The whole mixture is then thoroughly combined and the horse is given one cupful of this mixture twice a day with feed, along with 1 liter a day of rosehips tea. The above batch would last about twenty-four days and you will need to continue for at least forty-five days, which should see him well on the road to recovery. In severe cases, you may need to make up further batches to be administered for a further forty-five days to restore the horse to health.

Briefly, the rationale behind this particular blend of herbs is as follows:

- Borage and rosehips assist in restoring and rebuilding adrenal gland and kidney function.
- Dandelion leaf and root, along with kelp and fennel will restore and rebalance liver, pancreatic and thyroid functioning, which are the other partners with the kidneys and adrenal glands in the overall harmony of the metabolism.
- Nettle and rosehips are tonics that are high in iron.
- Hawthorn, rosehips and Bach Flower Rescue Remedy work on the heart, the shock and tap into the horse's core vitality.
- Garlic and rosehips are for protection against infection while the immune system is compromised.
- Chamomile restores parasympathetic nervous-system balance.

Each of the ingredients plays several roles and works in harmony with the others, and the overall effect is invariably dramatic in the extreme. The total cost of a three or four month program would be very reasonable – even if the mix was prepared professionally – definitely significantly less than conventional veterinary treatments, and significantly more effective.

Severely debilitated horses on the brink of death have recovered after treatment with this mixture, providing they are able to take the mix for the first five days.

Mild Stress-induced Debility

Continuing down the scale of debility, we have the horse that does not recuperate well after competition, for example the racehorse or three-day eventer that goes off his feed after competition and needs two or three weeks of coddling to prepare for another event. This type of horse is often very talented, but his temperament is such that his nervous and digestive systems are easily disturbed – unlike those other hardy souls that run around as soon as they get home and eat voraciously straight after a race or event. Herbs cannot change the highly strung horse or the 'poor-doer' into this latter type as so much of the personality and nervous-system type is involved – but we can protect the nervous and digestive systems from the effects of their personality as follows.

Prepare a dry mix of eight cups each of borage, dandelion leaf, hops flowers and nettle and four cups of rosemary leaves, add three cups of kelp granules and dampen down with 500 ml of vinegar-based maritime pine extract. A cup of this is to be fed twice a day added to morning and night feeds, and should be continued for twelve weeks at least in the first instance to evaluate its benefits, and then may be given as a regular feed additive while the horse is in full work. Also provide regular rosehips tea.

The rationale behind this mix is this:

- Borage and rosehips are again used to protect adrenal reserves and kidney function.
- Dandelion leaf and rosehips are for liver support.
- Nettle and rosehips are used as an iron tonic.
- Rosehips and pine bark support the immune system, the circulatory system and act as antioxidant tonics.
- Rosemary is useful for the specific and rather peculiar demands on the performance horse, which revolve around the demands on the muscles and the circulatory system in general as well as aspects of nervous energy.
- Hops regulate the 'over-revving' of the nervous system, which often remains for hours after the event and drains enormous amounts of energy from the nervous system quite out of proportion to the actual demands of the race or event itself.

Dealing with a Dull Coat

As all horse owners know, the condition of a horse's hair coat is a telling sign of his general level of health; a dull coat is indicative of a horse that is just not up to scratch healthwise. In itself the dull coat only says that the vitality is lower than normal due to metabolic imbalance, digestive efficiency or a toxic load. There are numerous possible underlying factors, which can include iron levels, lymphatic efficiency, kidney efficiency, circulatory efficiency or parasitic infestation, for example. Looking into the reasons for your horse's dull or 'starey' coat immediately you first notice it is the correct preventative approach, rather than waiting for a fully fledged illness to develop. Although there may not be any other obvious symptoms of ill-health, it is a warning of a metabolic imbalance that is best addressed.

A dull coat can be indicative of a worm burden in the horse, so follow an herbal worming program to eliminate this as the possible cause. This is best undertaken by introducing wormwood and garlic regularly into your horse's diet (see Chapter 4: Worming). Regularly add rosehips tea (a wonderful natural source of iron and vitamin C) to your horse's feed daily, also as a support for the blood, the liver, the kidneys, the adrenal glands, the circulation and the immune system.

Show-coat mix

Even when following such a regular care regimen, sometimes a horse's coat can become dull and using the following herbal 'cocktail' will just help to boost the horse's general health and act as a preventative for any imminent problems. The added bonus, of course, is that you can give a stunning shine to the show-horse's coat without having to resort to the dozens of expensive and potentially harmful coat 'shiners' that are commercially available.

The following herbal mix provides the healthy 'edge' to a horse's metabolism and gives a stunning shine to the coat.

Prepare a dry mix of 600 gm each of borage, nettle, fenugreek and dandelion leaf; 200 gm of chamomile and rosemary; and 1 kg of kelp. Add a cupful twice a day to feed for a few weeks to begin with and then one cupful a day as a maintenance dose.

You might consider giving a teaspoon of cod liver oil mixed into half a cup of one of the other grain oils (corn oil, sunflower oil, etc.) each day also, as part of your coat-conditioning program.

Other tips for creating and maintaining a healthy, shiny coat are based on the use of common sense: be very careful with, and very selective of, the shampoo you use to wash your horse and remember that all shampoo strips natural oils from the skin, so do not wash him too often. Any product you intend to use on a horse's skin should be tested on a small area and left overnight to check for any reactions. Swim your horse in salt water where possible.

Remember, it is normal for a horse to grow a thicker coat in winter.

Many people try all sorts of methods to make a competition horse lose a thick coat, even resorting to chemical feed additives. If you maintain his health at peak levels, then any hair coat he grows will be shiny and healthy. Appropriate rugging (not over-rugging) will help to lay the hair down so the coat looks sleek. If the horse gets extremely hairy and sweating in competition is a concern, then clipping is necessary; keeping his health at optimum levels will mean that the hair coat growing back will be shiny and healthy in appearance.

Very many coat problems are a result of our own interference (over-caring) and very many of them also are difficult to fix once an abnormal pattern has begun. Basically, there is no better recipe for a gleaming coat than optimum health and, as stated, natural herbal products are a readily available, cheap and effective alternative to the many topical and internal commercial coat 'shiners' on the market.

11 Basic Recipes

These basic herbal recipes are provided as a guide only. Preceding sections provide details on creating overall excellent health and dealing with specific conditions.

Rosehips Tea

4–6 rosehips teabags or 1–4 tablespoons of granules (1–2 tablespoons for maintenance, 3–4 if treating a condition or if the horse is not well). Add 1 liter of boiling water, allow to cool and use half to dampen the morning feed and half to dampen the evening feed.

Chamomile Tea

A handful of the dried flowers can be added directly to the feed or make up as a tea using 4–6 chamomile teabags or 2–4 tablespoons of the dried flowers to 1 liter of boiling water. Allow to cool and use as with the rosehips tea above.

Tendon, Ligament, Scar-tissue Poultice

- Fresh comfrey leaves
- Linseed oil

Blend several comfrey leaves with enough linseed oil to make it the consistency of a pesto. Place on gauze and wrap over the area, being careful how you bandage. Replace as needed. *Do not* use this poultice for broken skin or over a wound.

Drawing Poultice

- Slippery elm powder
- Castor oil

Castor oil alone is an excellent drawing agent. Begin by mixing several tablespoons of the slippery elm powder into a paste with the castor oil. Add more of each as required until you have a suitable amount of the mix for the area required. Place on gauze and wrap over the area being careful how you bandage.

Antiseptic/Styptic

- 100 ml each of extracts of yarrow and calendula
- Twenty drops of Bach Flower Rescue Remedy

Yarrow is a styptic herb, which acts to seal small blood vessels and reduce the bleeding while at the same time providing an energy boost to the physical nervous system. Calendula is an excellent general-purpose antiseptic, which will allow the body to gently control and expel any potentially infective agents.

Tendon and Bone Mix

- 4 kg each of freshly ground linseed and freshly ground white French birdseed millet
- $\frac{1}{2}$ kg yarrow

- $\frac{1}{2}$ kg kelp
- Prepare 2 liters of comfrey root extracted into organic cider vinegar, along with twenty drops of Bach Flower Rescue Remedy

One cup twice a day of this mix is added to morning and night feeds along with 20 ml twice a day of the extract and continued for six weeks or more after the disappearance of the last of the symptoms or evidence of injury. One cup a day as a maintenance dose.

Internal Ulcer and Scours Mix

Make up 1 liter of chamomile tea. To this add one third of a cup of slippery elm powder. Mix this into a paste using as much of the chamomile tea as necessary. Add in ten drops each of the Bach Flower Remedies impatiens and walnut. Include this in the feed daily and use the remaining tea to dampen down the feed. This should be continued for twelve weeks to give the gastro-intestinal system a chance to rebalance itself.

Show-coat Mix

- 600 g each of borage, nettle, fenugreek and dandelion leaf
- 200 g each of chamomile and rosemary
- 1kg kelp

Add one cupful twice a day to feed for a few weeks to begin with, then one cupful a day as a maintenance dose.

You might consider giving a teaspoon of cod liver oil mixed into a half cup of one of the other grain oils (corn oil, sunflower oil, etc.) each day also, as part of your coat conditioning program.

Hoof Oil

- 250 ml of linseed oil (very good for hoofs anyway)
- 1.5 ml arnica extract
- 6 ml each of rosemary oil, wintergreen oil, white willow and equisetum (horsetail) extract

- 15 ml comfrey extract
- 14 ml kelp extract
- Ten drops of Bach Flower Rescue Remedy

This combination will maximize health and healing in the hoof. The oil is applied to the whole hoof, sole and around the coronet twice daily.

Anemia Mix

- 500 g each of kelp, borage, nettle, red clover and rue
- 1 kg yarrow
- Prepare 1 liter of comfrey root extracted into organic cider vinegar, along with twenty drops of Bach Flower Rescue Remedy (or use two fresh comfrey leaves a day).
- Prepare 1 liter of hawthorn and maritime pine bark extracted into organic cider vinegar.

Feed one cupful twice a day of this mixture and 10 ml twice a day of each of the vinegar-based extracts. Also include $\frac{1}{2}$ liter of rosehips tea twice daily in the horse's feed.

Chest and Immunity Mix

- 150 g elecampane as support for the muscular power of the lungs and as a provider of allantoin.
- 300 g fenugreek seed as a source of vitamin A, as a tonic and restorative to the mucous membranes, especially in the upper respiratory system, and as a lymphatic tonic.
- 300 g kelp as a source of trace elements and mucilage to support the immune system and to provide assistance with softening and soothing the linings within the airways.
- 150 g marshmallow as a demulcent to soften and soothe irritations within the bronchi.
- 150 g mullein, which helps moderate the tickly irritations in the nasal passages.

- 150 g yarrow as a high-iron herb, also assists blood quality by supporting the red blood cell production and is a central-nervous-system tonic and astringent.
- 150 g nettle as a major boost to the iron levels available to the blood to help with the oxidation of the infective agents.

Plus

- 1.5 kg fresh, peeled organic garlic cloves
- 100 ml of maritime pine bark extract
- 300 g of rosehips granules
- 50 ml of an extract of coltsfoot (not essential but it will sometimes help as an expectorant).
- 100 g of thyme if the problem seems to be more localized in the throat than the bronchi or the sinuses.
- Ten drops each of the Bach Flower Remedies: olive, hornbeam and wild rose.

Extract these into enough organic cider vinegar to cover them, adding vinegar as the herbs swell (see Chapter 2: Vinegar-based Extracts). Allow it to steep for 5–6 weeks. Strain the herbs from the liquid, pressing the dregs to remove all the liquid. Add 10 ml of the resulting liquid twice a day to the horse's feed. Give the mixture for at least six weeks after the onset of symptoms.

Allergic Rhinitis Mix

- 100 g chamomile (as support for the parasympathetic nervous system, which is involved in the over-enthusiastic immune-system response underlying all allergic problems).
- 200 g euphorbia, which is very specific for the upper respiratory sneezing and snorting response.
- 1 kg minced fresh horseradish, which in its fresh form is a wonderful support and tonic to the mucosa of the upper respiratory system as well as wonderful for clearing the blood of elevated histamine levels.
- 200 g vervain as the characteristic nervine applicable to the horse that tends to be overly sensitive to external stimuli.
- 1 kg fresh, peeled organic garlic cloves

- 200 g fenugreek
- 200 g kelp
- 100 g marshmallow
- 100 g mullein
- 200 g nettle
- 100 g maritime pine bark
- 200 g rosehips
- 100 g yarrow
- Ten drops each of the Bach Flower Remedies: walnut for sensitivity and impatiens for the energy of over-reactivity.

Extract these into enough organic cider vinegar to cover them, adding vinegar as the herbs swell (see Chapter 2: Vinegar-based Extracts). Allow it to steep for 5–6 weeks. Strain the herbs from the liquid, pressing the dregs to remove all the liquid. Add 10 ml of the resulting liquid twice a day to the horse's feed. Give the mixture for at least six weeks after the onset of symptoms.

12 Case Studies

The following case studies are compiled from the files of the Bathurst Traditional Medicine Centre (Robert McDowell's herbal practice).

Buck

Endurance horses enjoy the very best of care from their owners, who, in order to compete in their sport successfully, must know their horses very well, particularly with regard to general health and fitness levels. Riders and horses naturally establish a close partnership and Buck and his owner have just such a close rapport.

Buck is a well-campaigned and very successful endurance horse (a thirteen-year-old buckskin 7/8 Arab) and the pair had been in training for the previous three years to compete in the Tom Quilty – Australia's grueling, annual, 100-mile endurance ride. Four days before they were due to leave for the ride's location in another state, Buck came down with a severe bout of colic in the middle of an 80-kilometer ride.

The owner said he was traveling well at the halfway vet check and then, at the next checkpoint as he unsaddled Buck, the horse went down. He had a history of mild colic attacks but this time seemed far more serious, with Buck lying down on his side, his neck stretched out and body rigid with the pain. The on-course vets immediately got him to his feet, setting him up on IV drips to get fluid into him (6 liters over three hours) and administered muscle relaxants to relieve the gut spasms. He did not seem to rally significantly and was transported as soon as possible to a nearby veterinary hospital. More fluids were given but he still had not passed manure in over three hours. Buck had improved enough to be sent home after six hours, but still did not pass manure until he had been at home for another two hours.

The next day he seemed to be over the worst of the attack and slowly to be picking up. The owner kept a close eye on his partner over the next few days and was worried that the horse still seemed depressed and lethargic, with a diminished appetite.

A few days later, he took Buck to a veterinary hospital to be checked again and, after a number of tests, was told there was no apparent cause for the colic attack, nor was there any solution to the horse's subsequent failure to rally. The only suggestion they could offer was that the horse's gut had been scarred by worm infestation early in his life, causing irreparable damage. The vet's recommendation to the owner was to have Buck put down, because he felt that the gut problems were too severe and untreatable to allow the horse to return to a useful or comfortable life.

Not willing to consider this end for his partner of many thousands of kilometers, the owner sought alternatives. A colleague suggested he contact Bathurst Traditional Medicine Centre (BTMC) and he was duly assured that there was a strong possibility of returning Buck to good health: they just had to use herbal treatments to 'reline' his stomach.

Buck was prescribed a liquid herbal mix containing the herb gentian and the Bach Flower Remedies rock rose, walnut, vine and Bach Flower Rescue Remedy. The owner was instructed to add chamomile tea to Buck's feed twice daily and slippery elm bark powder made into a paste, once a day. The herbal mix was administered for one month and the chamomile tea and slippery elm continued for twelve weeks. The owner was pleased to notice Buck gradually returning to his usual bright self over the next few weeks, although it took three months for his full recovery.

However, quite a recovery it was! The horse carried his owner easily over two 40-kilometer endurance rides, followed by two absolutely grueling 80-kilometer rides, both of which earned the pair a placing! Buck is now in the full bloom of health, with no recurrence of the problem (except for a minor hiccup on spring feed that was cured with a bottle of beer!) and is just starting his training for the current year's endurance season.

Kachét

When Kachét – a nine-year-old Arab mare – was diagnosed with fibrotic ossifying myopathy, the owner was told it was the end of the road for her as a dressage horse. She was advised to either put the mare in foal, pleasure walk her only, or completely retire her because there was nothing that could be done for the mare as the condition was permanent and would deteriorate.

The condition occurred in one of the mare's hind limbs, about twelve inches above the hock, and was brought on by a tear in the muscle. At the site of the tear, calcifications began to form, which severely inhibited forward, engaged movement. The condition can be quite painful.

The owner was told that surgery was an option but that there was a 50% chance the operation would worsen the condition. Unwilling to give up on the mare, she began looking for alternative options.

She contacted Bathurst Traditional Medicine Centre and a homeopath living in her home state who works with horses, and embarked on a course of treatment they felt could help the mare. The homeopath recommended strong doses of homeopathic arnica in the early stages of treatment and BTMC prescribed an herbal bone and tendon mixture. The herbal mix was continued for eighteen weeks and Kachét is now happy and pain-free.

The owner noticed marked improvements after a few weeks and, over time, the calcification at the site has broken down and the muscle healed. There were no side effects from the treatment, nor has there been any recurrence of the original problem.

Kachét is back in full work and the pair is again competing successfully in dressage competition.

Bracket Jack

Bracket Jack was a seventeen-year-old Thoroughbred, a successful national showjumper with numerous distinguished trophies and titles to his name. However, after his early success, he became recognized in showjumping circles as a 'difficult' horse that had become inclined to explode under pressure and to run-out at the big jumps unless ridden strongly and competently. His career had started to disintegrate as he got hotter and hotter and harder to manage. The owners eventually decided to relegate him to the pasture for an indefinite spell.

After Jack spent more than twelve months languishing in a pasture, he was advertised for sale, all aspirations to return him to the showjumping circuit abandoned. Many potential owners came to trial him, attracted by his fame and achievements, only to leave again after he refused a jump, bolted, or shied. After twelve months, the horse was sold to a lady who wanted to compete at low levels on an educated jumper, and who sensed a deep fear and insecurity in the horse.

When she got him home, on the ground he was wonderful to have around: quiet and obedient. Under saddle he became a neurotic, dangerous individual. Knowing his history and sensing that the real Jack was the 'person' she saw on the ground, the new owner felt there must be a way to overcome his overwhelming fear of being ridden, otherwise he was not going to be a viable proposition for her.

She began by giving the horse an herbal nerve tonic prescribed by BTMC, which was to work on nourishing and rebalancing Jack's nervous system to allow his true temperament to emerge. Jack's tonic was a mixture given in his feed as an additive, containing the herbs vervain, hops, chamomile, valerian and passion flower, along with homeopathic ingredients.

Everyone was amazed by the initial result: within mere days he was calmer and much less anxious, acting as though he could focus better on the job at hand without reacting to every little outside stimulus. To the delight of his owner – who had been concerned she might have to rely on the herbs indefinitely – Jack's calmness remained after the tonic was reduced and then discontinued altogether. It appeared that Jack's level of fear had permanently abated and even over jumps he was much calmer. His propensity to rush out of control had all but disappeared and any speed seemed more the result of his newfound exuberance than fear.

However, he was showing some signs of stiffness and soreness after work – understandable in a horse of his age with his history. The owner again contacted BTMC to devise an herbal remedy, and was provided with another mix containing apple cider vinegar, millet, linseed, yarrow, equisetum (horsetail), comfrey, arnica and white willow bark, and homeopathic healing stimulants. This remedy was also fed as a food additive and the dose was slowly reduced to a 'management' amount after the initial higher dose treatment. As an immediate result of the herbal remedies, Jack became rounder and softer through the back and was more willing to jump. The slight, shifting soreness completely disappeared.

The current result is a happy, calm – to his former owners completely unrecognizable – horse that is delighted to partner his new owner. His coat is glowing, his eyes are bright and the pair recently competed in their first local show to walk away with a large handful of blue ribbons!

Pepper

Two neighbors took pity on Pepper, a nineteen-year-old chestnut mare, that had taken to hanging about in a corner of a pasture over the road from their house. Pepper's owner had become elderly and frail and was no longer able to get about on the farm. The mare was not moving around much but seemed to be in reasonable shape physically, but they began to notice over a period of weeks that she was getting poor. They put it down to the sparse feed, but then Pepper went down a few days later and they then found she was suffering from an advanced case of founder, with her hooves in a shocking condition.

They contacted the owner, who was unable to assist and, while very sorry for what had happened, could only suggest that Pepper be put down. He was very pleased when they asked if they could take her on and try to fix her problems. They contacted BTMC, where they had been human patients for a number of years, and were given the following treatment program.

The first step was to treat the inflammation with the herbal anti-inflammatory mix, which had Pepper up, walking and feeding within three days. They administered 15 ml twice a day, along with some carrot, celery, bread and apple – partly for the vitamins and partly as treats to get her to take the medicine.

The next step was to begin applying the hoof oil treatment three times a week after cleaning her feet because they had discovered that all four hooves were rotten and badly infected. Extra white willow bark extract helped further with the pain, which was being managed well by the end of the first month.

Over the following months the anti-inflammatory mix dosage was reduced to 10 ml twice a day and they massaged her limbs twice a week (especially the rear tendons, which had shortened) using goanna oil – an Australian bush remedy.

Pepper's hooves regrew steadily at a rate of about a quarter of an inch a month and were filed and shaped as required. She was walked regularly and the new owners were riding her within six months.

Pepper's hooves were still sensitive and the owners locked her away from the spring growth as a precaution after she relapsed slightly. After eleven months, her medicine has been reduced to 10 ml every other day and she is ready for shoeing. The plan is to continue her medication for a couple of months after she has been shod and then stop the internal treatment altogether.

Pepper was on the verge of being put down when these compassionate people took over her care and she is now a beautiful healthy horse with a future.

Jackson

Jackson is a young Thoroughbred that came from a very well-known racing stud. He was in very good condition when the owner purchased him but had been rejected for racing as a two-year-old, even though the stud farm had paid AU$45,000 for him. Apparently he had not even had a racing trial because he was very timid and suffered from recurring gut problems they had been unable to control, which is truly amazing considering the highly qualified team of vets employed at this stud farm.

Despite being fed at consistent times each day with the best quality feeds, he suffered several very severe bouts of compaction colic requiring two extended stays in an equine veterinary hospital – one of four days and one of five days duration. Even following his very careful reintroduction to feed, the problem continued to recur, almost always after exercise. With traditional medicine having failed the owner opted to try an alternative approach and contacted BTMC. The horse has not had a problem since!

Jackson's treatment consisted of three cups of chamomile tea mixed with half a cup of slippery elm bark, fed for twelve weeks. Along with this, he is fed a natural diet of chaff, lucerne chaff, bran mash, oats and lucerne hay, as well as one tablespoon of brewer's yeast and a cup of canola oil (similar to sunflower or safflower oil) a day added to his feed. He also has free access to natural rock salt. He is maintained on a natural worming program because the owner has continued to avoid chemicals wherever possible.

Jackson is now a show hack; his coat looks fabulous and his general condition is A1. The owner says that he is also now a much more confident horse and this aspect of his character continues to make headway as he has more training and experience with clinics, lessons, shows, etc.

This is rather incredible, when you consider that this horse – when only three years of age – was a day away from being put down as a 'hopeless proposition'!

Shalimar

Shalimar was a nine-year-old pure-bred Arabian, purchased, in foal, by the owners as an addition to their stud's band of broodmares. She was unbroken and had apparently not been handled much, with a habit of snaking her neck, snapping her teeth and threatening to kick at humans who came too close.

Turned into a pasture with another broodmare, Shalimar was aggressive with the other horse, biting at her and chasing her off if she approached. She foaled after being at her new residence for two months. Her temperament worsened as she set out to protect the colt and was unwilling to allow the owners anywhere near him, while he, naturally, was showing signs of being as nervous and suspicious as his dam. As the months wore on, the owners had to resort to using food to tempt her and the foal into a small paddock to check them over as she would no longer suffer being caught – and trying to corner her was at best a dangerous business.

The owners contacted BTMC and were prescribed an herbal mixture for nervous rehabilitation, which was added to her daily feeds. To the owners' amazement and delight, after a month on the mix both mare and foal had calmed down immeasurably, with the mare allowing them to approach within a few feet. Eventually (after two months) she allowed them to catch her, after many hours spent just standing close to her, talking to her, stroking her and hand-feeding her titbits. As his dam learned to relax, the foal also allowed himself to be approached and now stands calmly to be caught and handled, although he is still very suspicious of any sudden moves. The mare is also learning to socialize with her pasture mate (and foal) and very rarely shows any sign of aggression.

The herbal mix has since been discontinued and this mare remains changed from a tense, highly-strung, suspicious horse that thought she had to be aggressive with humans and horses alike, to a (still suspicious!) broodmare that is far more relaxed around people.

Carmelita

A seven-year-old Quarter Horse mare, Carmelita had developed an itchy skin condition that the owners had failed to get under control using conventional treatments, like anti-inflammatory creams, washes and injections. The itch, characterized by lumps over her back and withers that sometimes wept pus, was always present in some form but seemed to worsen in summer. She had suffered from the condition, which seemed to get worse every year, for three years. They had also tried for the past two seasons to get the mare in foal: she had failed to fall pregnant the first year and slipped the foal in the early stages the second year.

Looking desperately for alternatives to deal with the skin condition, they contacted BTMC as a last resort, otherwise they felt the kindest thing was to have the mare destroyed as they could see no other solution and she really seemed to be suffering.

Carmelita was prescribed chamomile and rosehips tea in her feed twice daily and given an herbal mix containing nettle and dandelion. She was also sprayed daily with a weak chamomile tea mixture to which was added some colloidal silver, which seemed to provide immediate relief from the itchiness. The owners were also advised to add garlic and molasses to her diet on a regular basis.

Within a month there were signs of improvement: the mare was far more comfortable and the lumps were drying up, shrinking and disappearing. The condition gradually vanished over six months and the herbal mix was discontinued. She receives rosehips and chamomile tea along with garlic and molasses in her regular feeds, and there has been no recurrence of the problem.

As an added bonus, the mare went into foal the next spring and gave birth to a beautiful filly after a problem-free pregnancy.

Harry

Harry is a fat, gray child's pony of indeterminate breeding but indefatigable good nature. He had been in the owners' family since he was a youngster and had taught four of the owners' children, a large number of neighboring children and three or four enthusiastic adults to ride during his long and continuing career.

The owners thought he was about eighteen years of age, but no one really knew how old he was when they had acquired him. Every year since he was about eight he had suffered from founder with the onset of the spring feed. This had never been a major drama as the problem was never allowed to become severe; he was simply removed to a gravel yard, given phenylbutazone for a week or so and the laminitis disappeared until the next year.

In his eighteenth (or so) year he had the usual founder attack and the usual steps were taken. This year, however, he grew listless and went off his feed (the handful of chaff and carrots he was allowed daily) about four days after the first sachet of bute. Thinking it was the pain, the owners rang the vet to see whether they should increase the dose of anti-inflammatory. To their surprise, they were asked to bring the pony down to the surgery immediately, because it sounded as though he may have had 'bute toxicity'. On arrival he was tested and the tests were sent off to be analyzed in four to five days. In the meantime he was hospitalized and kept under observation as there was really nothing else that could be done. To the owners' horror, they were told that if the condition was what they suspected, then it would probably be fatal because the pony's intestinal lining would rupture. Most horses do not recover.

For the next few days, Harry was still not eating or drinking and was on an IV drip to keep his fluid levels up. He seemed miserable but not in extreme distress, however the vet warned the owners that this could change at any minute and to be prepared for the worst. Then, on day five, he perked up and ate a molasses-dipped carrot offered to him by his owners on their twice-daily visit! Slowly his appetite returned. In the meantime, the test results indicated that it had indeed been bute toxicity but tough little Harry had beaten the odds.

Two days later – at home now – Harry suffered a severe attack of founder. The vet said this was probably stress-induced but now they were unable to give him bute for the pain. It looked like Harry might lose the battle after all and the vet's recommendation was to have him put down if the pain seemed to increase.

At the suggestion of friends, BTMC was contacted urgently and Harry was prescribed large doses of an herbal anti-inflammatory, as well as a specially formulated bone and tendon herbal mix, and the owners were instructed to rub herbal hoof oil into his feet twice daily. The pain decreased markedly over two days and the attack seemed to be under control by the end of a week.

The vet was amazed at this tough little pony's recovery from the brink yet again, and contacted BTMC for more information on the anti-inflammatory mix, which apparently he is now using for many of his clients.

Harry's back in full work, teaching a five-year-old girl to sail over cavaletti and seems none the worse for his ordeal. The owners have replaced their bute sachets with a permanent bottle of herbal anti-inflammatory in the barn and use this for all their other horses' 'little ills' as well.

PART 3
Materia Medica of Herbs

The Actions of Herbs

As promised in Chapter 1 and for your reference and interest, we provide the following (simplified) listing of the actions of herbs. The idea with this list is to firstly read it through once without trying to remember much and just note those terms that seem to make sense. Later on you can look up specific herbs and their actions – either in the listing below or in other herbal texts – to give you further insights into what sorts of things you may expect from them.

Alteratives

These are blood cleansers or blood purifiers.

'Alterative' has become a word to describe the blood's processes of cleaning. Alteratives will be prescribed when infection is present or the remains of an earlier infection have not been completely removed. This process of cleansing is the last stage in the resolution of the disease process.

With modern antibiotic therapy, body wastes from infection are buried within body tissue rather than eliminated or expelled. Most antibiotics do not kill pathological invaders; they reduce the ability of the infecting organisms to proliferate and breed. The need to remove toxic waste products resulting from infection is ignored by scientific medicine.

Under the prodding of alterative herbs, lazy body systems stir into more positive activity, cell metabolism is more complete and efficient and accumulated waste departs somewhat obviously.

The action of alteratives always causes elimination of some kind, so if you notice foul breath, strange smelling (or loose) stools or urine, strange smelling sweat, pimples, boils or other skin discharges at the resolution stage of treatment, this will be the alteratives at work.

Herbs rich in iron, sulfur, chlorine and silica are alteratives.

Every student of herbal medicine must appreciate the difference between disease symptoms and elimination symptoms. Your horse will feel better and show more vitality each day as elimination proceeds, in complete contrast to feeling worse and less vital as a disease process continues.

Garlic and molasses, both high in iron and sulfur, are the simplest and most effective all round alteratives to use for horses.

Anodynes

Herbal anodynes will be found relieving pain spasms, improving blood and nerve supply and sending stronger and clearer signals on when to rest and when to be active again.

As herbalists we prescribe to relieve the cause of pain, not the pain itself. Pain is the barometer of the quality of an illness and there is a vast difference between relieving pain and blocking pain.

Accepting pain as a monitor of just how sick, over-tired, or over-strained a body part is allows you to make better judgments on appropriate pain-reduction treatments. There are pains that need movement and release of pressure and pains that need rest. There is also a difference between hot pain and cold pain, which must be recognized. Pain can also be caused by pressure, immobility and posture.

Anodynes reduce the intensity of pain, while narcotics block the recognition of pain signals. Herbal anodynes can reduce pain by relieving spasms in organs – for example, chamomile and valerian are herbs that act as anodynes in some circumstances.

Penetrating resinous and oily substances can warm body tissues by quickly bringing blood to the area. In disease processes where warmth and extra nourishment will reduce the pain, lavender, wintergreen and rosemary oils can be effective.

If pain recurs in the same area, inflammatory processes may be at work, with fluid accumulation, pressure and swelling producing local pain. The primary source of pain may be from the blood, as in the case of rheumatic processes where heat and friction often produce more pain. For such cases, sedatives like vervain, hops and St Johns wort are more often prescribed. These herbs calm the excitability of the physical nerve signals. Over-stimulation of the nerve fibers will produce acid wastes, which cause a discomfort perceived as pain.

Antipruritics

Antipruritics reduce itching.

After pain the most annoying symptom must surely be that of the itch that scratching cannot relieve. There are many underlying causes of itching, from liver inefficiencies, to allergies, bites and stings.

The underlying causes must always be sought and treated, but certain herbs will relieve the itch by either chemically neutralizing protein or acid stings (vinegar or dock leaves) or soothing eczema and related dermatitis (chamomile or aloe vera).

Antiseptics

A germ-free environment is unachievable and undesirable; a natural balance between beneficial and non-beneficial micro-organisms is what is required.

Antiseptics not only reduce the likelihood of abnormal population imbalances, they also work by reducing the pathogen's ability to replicate.

It is the waste products of pathogen metabolism that makes the body unwell.

Much of the body's defenses depend on well-balanced and clean blood. Therefore, alteratives and antiseptics may not only be necessary together, but also one may not be completely effective without the other. Calendula and thyme are examples of antiseptic herbs.

Antispasmodics

Antispasmodics relieve pain by reducing spasm.

These herbs often work at the level of the nervous system, as with the nervines like hops, vervain, valerian, chamomile, skullcap and mugwort.

There are also other herbal antispasmodics, like black cohosh, which break up spasms by metabolic action rather than via the nerves.

Rosemary oil and massage will help reduce spasm by improving blood supply to affected areas.

Astringents

Astringents tone, tighten, contract and bind – but do not dry.

These herbs remove fluid from an area and redistribute it to where it needs to be. Fluids can be forced out of the immediate zone by a sudden or strong tissue contraction. Fluids can also be retained when tissues tighten, bind and contract.

Aldosterone is the natural fluid-regulating hormone.

If a lot of fluid is being drained, your horse should be urinating more freely. If your horse does not sweat freely, astringents may form part of the treatment. Astringents are also often added to mixtures to improve the elasticity of muscles and ligaments.

Astringent herbs like yarrow are prescribed for internal and external hemorrhages and for scouring. They are also prescribed for edema or fluid retention in joints or other areas of injury.

Herbs high in tannins are astringent and all plants produce some tannin as a part of their growth process. The bark of the oak is used to this day in tanning leather (driving the fluid out of the hides to preserve them). Our normal cup of tea is high in tannin and, in excess, can inhibit kidney function by restricting the free flow of fluids through the kidneys.

You may find your horse chewing on something odd at times, which, when you sample it, may be very drying on the tongue, like sucking on a lemon. In such a case, your horse is self-medicating by taking an astringent.

Bitters

Bitter herbs act as a tonic and stimulant to the mucosal linings within the mouth, the esophagus and the stomach.

Bitter herbs may be prescribed when blocked or under-active gall and digestive organs are diagnosed; in these cases the bitters will stimulate production of enzymes, bile and stomach acids. Gentian is a common bitter digestive tonic for use with humans.

The bitter taste in many leafy greens like watercress or dandelion leaf is the taste of choline, which is a liver tonic.

As a general rule, grazing animals, whose digestive systems are very different from the omnivorous variety like those of humans, do not need the traditional bitter tonics.

In all the variety of weeds, grasses and leaves upon which your horse will graze naturally, there must be dozens of more appropriate bitter herbs than we can possibly prescribe.

Carminatives

Carminatives act to warm and comfort and cause better internal blood supply in the digestive tract.

Carminatives produce a very soothing and antiflatulent effect in the stomach and intestines, thereby improving digestion.

They will often contain iron and phosphorus and common examples are horseradish, ginger, peppermint and chilli (how warm do you want to be?).

Grow a little mint and horseradish about the place or in your hedgerow for your horse to seek out; make a very dilute tea from fresh ginger and chamomile to treat your horse after a bout of colic.

Cathartics

These are purgatives or very strong laxatives.

This class of herbs is seldom used for horses.

However, if there is a bowel blockage, an oil drench can be helpful and the most dramatic and, in many ways, the safest of these is castor oil.

Demulcents and Emollients

Demulcents soothe and soften tissues within the body: the digestive tract, vagina, bladder, kidneys, lungs and sinuses, for example.
Emollients soothe the outside, in the form of oils and creams mostly.

Substances with these actions reduce pain and irritation and make the skin or internal structures more comfortable. They also reduce itch or irritation from bites and burns.

Slippery elm, aloe vera juice, marshmallow and comfrey are examples of herbs that work equally well as demulcents and emollients.

Fenugreek soothes the mucosal lining within sinus cavities. Pawpaw ointment is excellent for irritated sensitive tissue around the eyes, nose, mouth, anus, sheath or vagina of your horse.

Mucilaginousness (stickiness or a glue-like quality) is the common denominator in all these herbs, which promotes healing by reducing inflammation, roughness and irritation, thereby reducing pain and discomfort. It also reduces damage by contact with any overly acid body fluids, mucous linings or skin.

Treatments internally and externally should be continued until real healing has been established and completed - usually six to eight weeks of daily use constitutes a complete course. Otherwise, if treatment is interrupted, the course may need to be repeated.

Diuretics and Diaphoretics

Herbs with these actions push fluid out of the body.

Diuretics operate through the kidneys.

Diuretics contain high levels of potassium, silica and perhaps iron and sulfur as supporting partners. Equisetum (horsetail), juniper and celery are examples of diuretic herbs.

Potassium operates at the cellular level and acts to draw moisture from cells. In the body, potassium works in conjunction with sodium, which draws moisture into cells, and it is this flow of fluid both ways that is essential to cellular metabolism and health. Silica stimulates kidneys and bowels and the nerve supply to both.

At the start of diuretic treatments, urine will be somewhat darker, more odorous and even slightly irritating as fluid wastes are removed. There may also be chalkiness and cloudiness as gravel and tiny stones are dislodged.

Substances high in potassium also improve muscular strength and energy and all of them should be partnered with substances high in sodium in the correct balance, or damage to the kidneys can result. This is the problem with medical diuretics (often just chemical potassium compounds), which are totally unbalanced and always result in damage to kidneys and other systems with long-term use.

Celery and juniper together make a perfectly balanced herbal diuretic because celery is high in silica and sodium, and juniper is high in potassium. Bananas with rock salt is another, but do not force-feed either, just allow the horse access to both at the same time and let him choose.

Diaphoretics *encourage sweating or the passage of fluid through the skin.*

These treatments may initially alter the color or odor of perspiration as the body takes the opportunity to clear waste products from the pores and the lymphatic system and discharge them through the skin.

It is necessary for your horse to sweat to some degree no matter where he lives but a healthy skin will acclimatize itself quickly to its surrounding air temperature and humidity.

Of course, horses use sweating as their primary cooling mechanism but should sweat only as much as is necessary to regulate body heat and to aid kidney function as required.

Dandelion, fenugreek and mint are common herbs with active diaphoretic properties.

Emmenogogues

Emmenogogues will help to bring on estrus.

Emmenogogues can be helpful if, for some reason (such as prolonged male hormone treatments or other steroids), normal estrus is overdue. Emmenogogues are not abortifascients (which means 'causing abortion').

Pennyroyal is a powerful estrogen-containing plant, a common weed that should be included in your herbal hedgerow.

Febrifuges

Febrifuges bring out and encourage fever.

Chilli, cayenne pepper, ginger and mustard are common herbal febrifuges.

Your horse should be kept warm if you are treating with a febrifuge, as his susceptibility to chilling will increase while being treated.

Plants classified as febrifuges will include diaphoresis among their actions; although not strictly interchangeable terms, febrifuge and diaphoretic are often applied to the same plant.

Hepatics

Hepatics are liver tonics.

Some schools of alternative treatments for humans focus very heavily on the liver because it is seen by both eastern and western herbal medicine as being fundamental to both physical and emotional wellbeing. Even in our language we have some expressions that reflect the relationship between emotional states and the liver: the term 'liverish' signifies irritability, misery, pickiness, and crankiness – a sort of low-grade, cold, stewing anger.

As a rule, the liver in the horse does not play such a huge role in either their overall health or their emotional health, probably as a result of the simplicity of their diet and not having to break down all the toxins as is the case with humans. However, an over-stimulation of the liver – as a result of too much green feed in spring, or following shock – can result in scours.

Dandelion leaves and root are useful for horses in various mixes when the aim is to rebalance the metabolism and it can be valuable to the poor doer or the horse recovering from metabolic problems, shock or colic. St Mary's thistle is equally valuable.

In the horse, these hepatics are just really included to support the liver as a partner to other organs involved in aspects of digestion and metabolism.

Laxatives

Laxatives are substances often high in iron and sulfur that are helpful in normalizing bowel function.

Molasses and prunes are good examples of laxatives that soften feces. Other laxatives work by retaining fluid within the feces to prevent them drying out too much, for example liquorice and slippery elm. Still others work by stimulating the peristalsis within the bowel, for example senna and aloe vera.

If using laxative herbs, start slowly and gently and support the whole digestive system with chamomile at the same time. A cyclical pattern of constipation followed by the scours is usually harder to shift and more debilitating than the original problem and it is all too easy to produce such a pattern if you are impatient.

Nervines

The plant nervines balance both overly-active and under-active nervous-system responses and promote a calm two-way balance between action and relaxation.

Almost every professionally prescribed herbal treatment will contain an appropriate nervine.

When your horse's particular nervous system (see Chapter 4: The Types) is supported within a treatment program, the program will be more effective and produce a more rapid result.

The nervines you may become familiar with in treating your horse will include: chamomile, hops, hypericum, passion flower, valerian and vervain.

Plant nervines do not become an addictive necessity and nor do they reduce in their efficacy with exposure. Large doses are not harmful, just wasteful.

Most nervines contain varying amounts of magnesium, phosphorus and calcium with silica and some zinc plus trace minerals like bromine, iodine and selenium.

Rubefacients

Rubefacients act as irritants, which bring blood to an area (either on the surface or deeper) by over-stimulating blood vessels or nerves.

The word 'rubefacient' means literally 'to make red'.

Usually used externally, rubefacients are applied as a counter-irritant to an area that has already been made red by some other irritation or inflammation.

Sometimes a plant is both a rubefacient and a carminative. Wintergreen oil is both: it is warming and it makes the skin red.

Nettle is a mild rubefacient, while cajeput oil, mustard and chilli are much stronger ones. These herbs were often used in poultices or 'blisters' but there is never a need for, or value in, taking their action all the way to blistering, although this was common medical practice up until the early twentieth century.

These irritant substances must be kept away from body openings like nostrils, mouth, eyes, etc.

You should never use strong rubefacients on your horse's lower limbs. They cannot produce positive results because the limbs are not supported by sufficient circulation and blistering and sores will result with no positive outcome whatsoever.

Rubefacients may be needed when there is atrophy present in the big muscles of the body, following nerve damage or injury perhaps, or following forced immobilization. They can also be useful in conjunction with massage therapy after trauma to the spine. Treatment must be stopped as soon as obvious heat is observed in the area.

Vermicides and Vermifuges

Vermicides kill worms and creeping parasites; Vermifuges expel them from the body.

These actions are often both found in the same herb and, without exception, they have strong, bitter flavors.

The astringency and tannins present in these herbs cause contraction of the intestinal mucosa and the bitterness produces distaste in the parasite. The vermifuge effect then aids elimination of the dead or discouraged parasites through the bowels, along with their debris and waste products.

These herbs are prescribed in short bursts of treatment at a comparatively high dose compared to the usual herbal dose.

Aloes, garlic, male fern and wormwood are vermicides - with male fern being specific for hydatids, and wormwood for heartworm in dogs.

Vulnaries

The action of vulnaries is to repair damage to blood-vessel walls and surrounding tissues.

Arnica is one such herb and rue is another. Arterial repair requires more strongly astringent herbs like yarrow to deal with the pressure in these vessels.

Vulnaries are, therefore, used for bruising, even bone bruises and their combined actions will repair the damaged tissue, improve the circulation both to and from the damaged area and stimulate the lymphatic fluid drainage.

They should not be applied to broken skin as they may inhibit clotting.

The List of Herbs

It is hard to know where to stop when listing herbs and in the end one just draws the line arbitrarily!

We have tried to include descriptions of the most common and most useful herbs, as well as most of those mentioned in the treatments in the book. Those that are missing can be found in other texts.

Others herbs, which for your purposes are of minor importance, have been included to illustrate a particular action or make a point about application or cautions.

Alfalfa/Lucerne (*Medicago sativa*)

Parts used Aerial parts (the whole herb that appears above the ground).

Actions Carminative and digestive.

Contents Alfalfa is high in pectin, proteins, enzymes and amino acids. It contains vitamins A, B1, B2, C and K and useful amounts of potassium, magnesium, copper, cobalt and iron.

Utility Useful for: regulating an over-active, acidic and gassy digestive system; regulating the over-production of mucus; treating the over-activity in the nervous and immune systems; reducing over-sensitivity to insect bites.

Application Traditionally fed as a green hay or chaff as part of a standard diet. Can be made into a concentrated tea in boiling water (perhaps with chamomile) for internal treatment, or sprayed onto the animal after hosing down to soothe insect bites.

Cautions None.

Aloes (*Aloe vera*)

Parts used Juice from the leaves.

Actions Emollient, antipruritic and purgative.

Contents Contains mucilage, glycocides, sterols, saponins and resin.

Utility Aloe vera juice seals burnt, damaged or irritated skin from the air and promotes healing.

Application Apply the fresh juice immediately after branding or any other burn. It can also be used to soothe itchy or damaged skin giving instant relief. Encourage an aloes plant somewhere handy to your yards or stables and protect it from foraging horses. It is not for their internal treatment but for your first-aid use (do not forget it works just as well on your own burns, scalds, sores and itches).

Cautions Can be a strong purgative. Do not let your horses eat it in case you end up with a difficult case of scours.

Arnica (*Arnica montana*)

Parts used   Roots and dried flowers.

Actions   Astringent and vulnerary.

Contents   Lactones, flavonoids, thymol, arnicin and mucilage.

Utility   Quickly seals off damaged blood vessels while promoting circulation away from an injury site, thereby reducing blood and plasma leakage and promoting healing. In homeopathic dilution, used internally as a shock treatment.

Application   As an extract in creams and oils (usually 5% but for the lower limbs of horses this must be reduced to 1%, as higher concentrations will cause swelling). As a wash, 0.02% in water, after hosing down competition horses following heavy work.

Cautions   Do not put on an open wound as it will slow clotting and it is not antiseptic. Use sparingly on your horses' lower limbs as it will cause swelling and discomfort in such areas where there is limited circulation.

Borage (*Borago officinalis*)

Parts used   Aerial parts.

Actions   Diaphoretic, diuretic and tonic.

Contents   Borage is a particularly valuable source of mineral salts, especially sodium, potassium and calcium.

Utility   Adrenal, digestive, kidney, liver and blood tonic.

Application   The best general tonic for the competition horse in work as a regulator of adrenal reserves, temperature control and source of natural electrolytes, particularly potassium nitrate.

Cautions   None on cup-sized doses mixed with other feed, or in the hedgerow.

Buckwheat (*Fagopyrum esculentum*)

Parts used Leaves and seeds.

Actions Antihemorrhagic and vasodilator.

Contents The flavonoid glycocides rutin and quercetin (buckwheat is the commercial source of rutin).

Utility Strengthens and repairs blood-vessel walls (especially in the lungs and venous system).

Application Buckwheat should be seeded in your hedgerow for availability on demand and the seeds included with other grains on occasion. Routine use is indicated for horses with a history of bleeding.

Cautions None.

Calendula/Marigold (*Calendula officinalis*)

Part Used Flowers.

Actions Anti-Inflammatory, antiseptic, antifungal, astringent and vulnerary.

Contents High in vitamin A and contains a highly antiseptic essential oil.

Utility General-purpose antiseptic, applied externally.

Application Found in commercial ointments, usually 5%. Extremely useful as an ingredient (with yarrow) as an antiseptic/styptic mix in extract form for the first-aid kit. Useful in very diluted form as an eyewash.

Cautions Not to be given internally, except under the supervision of a qualified herbalist.

Castor Oil (*Ricinus communis*)

Parts used   Oil extracted from the seeds.

Actions   Purgative (laxative).

Contents   The seeds contain about 50% of fixed oil, the contents of which are largely glycerin and ricinoleic acid, which is peculiar to the plant.

Utility   Used in cases of colic, constipation, acute scours and sluggish digestion, as well as a drawing agent to clear mastitis in mares and to clear puncture wounds of debris as an anti-tetanus treatment.

Application   Externally: for mastitis apply to the teat after each feed (to be washed off before the foal's next feed); over a puncture or other dirty wound on a pad to be held in place by a plaster or bandage if possible.

Internally: to be given with paraffin oil in treating colic, other bowel blockages and constipation.

Cautions   A useful tonic to stimulate sluggish bowels in foals, for older horses and in emergency situations but only to be used judiciously and certainly not as a matter of regular practice.

Celery (*Apium graveolens*)

Parts used   Aerial parts fresh, or seeds dried.

Actions   Alkalizing, anti-Inflammatory, digestive, diaphoretic and diuretic.

Contents   Celery is an excellent source of sodium and silica, along with digestive enzymes. It is a useful source of phosphorous and other salts and the volatile oil has anti-fungal properties.

Utility In the treatment of stones (formations of calculi in kidneys, bladder, urethra or intestines); rheumatism and arthritis; and as a kidney, liver and adrenal tonic. Paired with juniper, celery is a perfectly balanced diuretic treatment.

Application As a fresh herb fed by hand, made available in a hedgerow or given as a tea made from the seed.

Cautions There are no cautions with the fresh herb, the seed however is very powerful and should be made into a tea with a maximum of one tablespoon a day.

Chamomile (*Anthemis nobilis*)

Parts Used Flowers (usually dried).

Actions Antispasmodic, carminative, digestive, tonic and nervine.

Contents High natural source of phosphorous and calcium compounds utilized by the nervous system. Contains also a volatile oil, tannic acid and a glucoside.

Utility Specifically nourishes all parasympathetic nervous-system functions. Chamomile therefore regulates: allergic reactions; sleep patterns; hormone levels; the gastro-intestinal system; the immune system; skin sensitivity; and coat appearance.

Application Chamomile is such a useful and general-purpose herb that it should be included as a small but regular ingredient in the normal diet. Most economically, this will be as an unstrained herb tea made with a quarter of a cup of flowers to $\frac{1}{2}$ liter of boiling water. This can be fed to a feeding mare for her foal, mixed with slippery elm powder for digestive problems, used to dampen feed or in a bran mash. Medicinal doses are double the above.

Cautions None.

Chickweed (*Stellaria media*)

Parts used   Fresh tops.

Actions   Demulcent and diaphoretic.

Contents   The ingredients of chickweed are not fully studied yet.

Utility   External application in a poultice to aid in drawing from boils or abscesses; in ointments for soothing skin problems; and the fresh juice for skin cancers.

Application   Specific for skin cancers on horses.

Cautions   The fresh juice can burn sensitive tissue if used too freely.

Comfrey/Knitbone (*Symphytum officinale*)

Parts used   Roots and leaves, fresh and dried.

Actions   Demulcent, emollient, stimulant to bone, connective tissue and cartilage repair, and vulnerary.

Contents   Comfrey is the highest plant source of vitamin B12 and allantoin (a cell proliferant). It is highly mucilaginous and contains phenolic acids, choline and tannins, along with pyrollizidine alkaloids.

Utility   As a healing agent for all damaged tissue, especially bones. Comfrey accelerates the normal healing processes and minimizes scarring. It is also valuable in the treatment of skin and bronchial conditions and has been used in the regulation of female hormones.

Application   Externally: comfrey is used in poultices, oils and creams. Internally: it is used as a component in bone and ligament injury and maturity applications. Herbalists also include comfrey in mixes aimed at repairing hard tissue abnormalities like scarring; adhesions; bone degeneration, spurs, nodules and calcification; and in mixes designed to stimulate retarded development of all types.

Cautions   Due to the presence of the alkaloids, comfrey is presently banned for internal use in Australia, as a result of excessively stringent controls applied to herbal and other alternative remedies. It is in fact perfectly safe for your horse in cup-sized doses as a vinegar extract, as one fresh leaf bruised to reduce the prickles or on demand as a hedgerow herb, but as a safety measure only dose as suggested in the specific recipes. As a poultice or for other external application it must be used with antiseptic herbs because it is not antiseptic in its own right.

Dandelion/Wet-The-Bed (*Taraxacum officinale*)

Parts used   Roots dried and leaves fresh or dried.

Actions   Alterative, bitter, carminative, digestive, diuretic and hepatic.

Contents   Vitamins A, B, C and D, potassium and calcium salts, manganese, sodium, sulfur and choline.

Utility   Stimulates liver function and bile production, pancreas and kidney function and, therefore, the digestive system in general. It cleans the blood and stimulates excretion processes through the bowel, kidneys and via the lymphatic system, as well as through the skin.

Application   Dandelion is an excellent spring tonic to cleanse the system after winter feed and assist in the digestion of fresh green growth.

It is also a major ingredient in rehabilitation and conditioning mixes, particularly if condition is lost due to the stress of competition. Dandelion is used to treat rheumatism, and a mixture of dandelion and alfalfa is excellent to reduce sensitivity to protein allergies.

Cautions   True dandelion must not be confused with the false type (sometimes called flatweed), both of which are often found together. The true dandelion has paler green, softer and less hairy leaves, which are sharply toothed; each flower stands on a single stem that is hollow and has white sap. The false dandelion is a darker green in color, hairy and has multiple flowers on a branching solid stem. Both have identical yellow flowers and seed heads. False dandelion is sometimes associated with stringhalt in Australia.

Devil's Claw (*Harpogophytum procumbens*)

Parts used   Tuber.

Actions   Analgesic, anti-inflammatory, antirheumatic and sedative.

Contents   Irodoid glycosides, flavonoids and phenolic acids.

Utility   Useful for arthritic, rheumatic and other pain control.

Application   An ingredient in primary anti-inflammatory mixes, in particular in the mix designed to replace phenylbutazone (see Chapter 4: Anti-inflammatories).

Cautions   Not advisable to give to mares in foal, as it can produce uterine contractions. Used alone, a dose of one tablespoon of root daily as an herb tea would be sufficient.

Echinacea (*Echinacea purpurea*)

Parts used   Aerial parts.

Actions   Alterative, antibacterial, antifungal, antiviral, immuno-stimulant and tonic.

Contents   Contains glycocides, polysaccharides, polyacetylenes, essential oils and flavonoids along with copper.

Utility   Specifically increases leukocolyte production in the blood and

clears deep-seated and toxic waste products of infection from the body.

Application   Included in treatments along with garlic to normalize immunity and the populations of abnormal organisms associated with infection. Specific for all blood poisoning and septicemia cases. Can be given as the dried herb in small quantities or as a vinegar extract.

Cautions   Not to be given in any situation where elevated white cell counts could be due to leukemia (cancer).

Equisetum/Horsetail (*Equisetum arvense*)

Parts Used   Aerial parts.

Actions   Anti-inflammatory, astringent, healer and mineral source.

Contents   Equisetum is the highest vegetable source of silica (in silicic acid) along with magnesium, phosphorous and calcium. It also contains several alkaloids, saponins, flavonoids and sterols, which assist in its healing action.

Utility   Equisetum is utilized for all bone repair and normalization treatments and also for reabsorbing any calcifications, including stones, spurs and nodules. Its secondary ingredients are utilized in the repair of the physical nervous system following trauma.

Application   The unique blend of ingredients supports all traumas to the skeletal and ligament structure of the horse along with the accompanying central and peripheral nervous system. It will also support the maturity of the structure in young animals, the recovery from rheumatoid and arthritic processes and the growth and health of hair, teeth and hooves. A half a cupful either as a dried herb or made into an herb tea is the maximum medicinal daily dose.

Cautions   Large doses of equisetum, especially if not balanced by other minerals, can cause the overly rapid breakdown of stones in the urinary tract, causing severe pain at times.

Elecampane (*Inula helenium*)

Parts used   Roots.

Actions   Diaphoretic, diuretic and tonic,

Contents   Allantoin, mucelage and silica.

Utility   Elecampane is a specific tonic to the muscular efficiency of the lungs, which, along with allantoin, makes it ideal to restore and

restimulate weakened respiratory function. Other uses include bone repair work (like comfrey) and it is a useful kidney tonic but not as good as rosehips.

Application Elecampane is included in all mixes aimed at improving the efficiency and immunity of the respiratory system.

Cautions None in medicinal doses, maximum one third of a cup a day.

Eucalyptus (*Eucalyptus globulus*)

Parts used Leaves.

Actions Antiseptic, antispasmodic, expectorant, stimulant and febrifuge.

Contents Volatile oils (including eucalyptol, terpineol and pinene), polyphenolic acids and flavonoids.

Utility A common ingredient in vapor treatments for colds and respiratory infections and in disinfectants and antiseptics.

Application Eucalyptus oil can be used with a source of steam in the stable to treat and protect against respiratory infections (much as we do with babies using a vaporizer). A few fresh leaves can be thrown in with bedstraw, or boiled and added to drinking water.

Cautions A few leaves only when given internally as a tea.

Fennel (*Foeniculum vulgare*)

Parts used   Fresh whole herb including the bulb, and seeds dried.

Actions   Carminative and digestive.

Contents   Anethole, flavonoids and coumarins.

Utility   Fennel stimulates the pancreatic acid and bile flow and has useful soothing properties for eye irritations.

Application   Fennel seeds are used in conditioning mixes where work, stress or illness has upset the metabolic balance. In such mixes they would almost always be accompanied by chamomile, dandelion and, perhaps, alfalfa and kelp to stimulate the other systems involved in digestive efficiency and balance. Can be given fresh, seeded in the hedgerow, as the dry seed, or made into a tea with boiling water and used to dampen feed or mash.

Cautions   None.

Fenugreek (*Trigonella foenum-graecum*)

Parts Used   Seeds.

Actions   Alterative, expectorant, diaphoretic, demulcent, febrifuge and tonic.

Content   Albumen (for the kidneys), vitamins A and B, choline, lecithin, minerals (especially iron and phosphates), mucilage, sugars and digestive enzymes (especially as sprouts, which can be made at home from seeds using a commercially-available sprouting system, or purchased from specialist greengrocers or health-food stores).

Utility   Specific as a tonic for the mucous membranes of the upper respiratory system and sinus, for the lymphatic system and for the pancreas.

Application   Fenugreek is used as a blood cleanser and tonic in the case of lymphatic-system stasis or sinus infection, irritation or congestion. Its diaphoretic and lymphatic stimulant properties make it important in the treatment of anhydrosis ('the puffs'). Although the seeds are extremely hard and will pass through our own gut without much sign of digestion, the horse's gut, being designed for grains and grasses, can break them down. The seeds can also be made into an herb tea or vinegar extract, ground to a powder, or sprouted. An appropriate dose is two tablespoons daily.

Cautions   None.

Garlic (*Allium sativum*)

Parts used   Bulbs (and tops when fresh).

Actions   Alterative, anti-infective, antifungal, antiviral and diaphoretic.

Contents   Approximately 80% of garlic consists of sulfur compounds - including allicin and aliin - along with volatile oils and the trace minerals zinc and copper.

Utility   Garlic is a natural antibiotic, bactericide and fungicide. It is

an alterative and fights infection, repels parasites internally and externally, increases bile flow and breaks up cholesterol in the blood vessels. Garlic will also repel worms (tapeworms and hookworms) internally and insects externally and reduces pathogenic organisms within the intestines while leaving the gut flora intact. It also stimulates brain function.

Application   Garlic is so generally applicable as a preventative and tonic that it should be fed routinely to all domestic horses. It can then be fed in larger doses while fighting specific pathogens. Whole cloves can be fed directly or steeped in molasses or honey to prepare medicinal oil of garlic. Four cloves daily is a satisfactory maintenance dose, which can be trebled in case of infection.

Cautions   Garlic can overload the liver if it is weakened as in cases of hepatitis or hepatic failure and is also contra-indicated in cases of pancreatitis. Otherwise there are no cautions.

Golden Seal (*Hydrastis canadensis*)

Parts Used   Roots.

Actions   Antiseptic, astringent and vulnerary to mucous membranes throughout the body.

Contents   Alkaloids, resins, vitamin A and volatile oils.

Utility   Soothing for mucosal inflammation and infections, drawing and antiseptic.

Application   Cleans wounds and aids discharge from surface eruptions, but its main utility for our purposes is as one of the ingredients in the eyewash along with celandine and rue.

Cautions   Must always be diluted in water for use in the eye. When given internally it can over-stimulate the liver.

Hawthorn (*Crataegus oxycanthus*)

Parts Used   Berries, leaves and flowers.

Actions   Cardiac tonic, coronary and peripheral vasodilator and hypotensive.

Contents   Contains flavonoids including rutin, procyanidine, phenolic acids, tannins and ascorbic acid.

Utility   Hawthorn is a heart and circulatory tonic that will regulate heart rate when it is has lost its normal rhythm because of shock, work stress or after a general anesthetic, for example.

Application   Hawthorn trees should be used as the principal structure of hedgerows. They offer protection for the herbs grown beneath them, as well as a physical barrier. Your horses will also nibble at the odd berry or leaf from time to time out of curiosity, or in response to instinctive requirements. Daily doses of hawthorn tea made with a quarter of a cup of dried berries steeped in $\frac{1}{2}$ liter of boiling water is useful for aiding in the treatment of navicular disease or laminitis, by improving circulation down to the hoof.

For medicinal purposes in treating our equine friends however, hawthorn has a unique function. It acts as a central-nervous-system tonic in cases of extreme depletion, i.e. after a major health and/or nervous-system episode such as going down in the trailer; a major accident; an operation; severe colic; a snake bite; starvation; severe pasture poisoning; or prolonged scours. In such a case, hawthorn will offer a major boost to the central nervous system and assist in the decision as to whether the animal should be put down or not. Give two doses of hawthorn extract (either the tea or vinegar-based, say 30–40 ml), spaced ten minutes apart, to which has been added Bach Flower Rescue Remedy. If this fails to produce a positive reaction within fifteen or twenty minutes, the animal has insufficient reserves to allow him to recover from the shock and the humane decision at this point is to put him down. Interestingly enough, the herb parsley acts in humans *in extremis* in exactly the same way and an extract of parsley was used in the Middle Ages by the 'paramedics' of the day for exactly the same purpose.

Cautions   None for your horse. However, do not attempt to use hawthorn to treat human heart conditions without professional advice.

Hops (*Humulus lupulus*)

Parts used   Female flowers.

Actions   Antispasmodic, nervine, sedative and tonic.

Contents   Volatile oils, flavonoids, resin, tannin and estrogenic substances.

Utility   Helpful in the nervous disposition characterized by a head that is too busy under stress and shows up as irritability, lack of control, restlessness or aggression.

Application   For such horses, a cupful of dried hops each day added to feed will serve to nourish this particular sort of nervous system and allow it to function more normally.

Cautions   There are no cautions for hops except that quite a number of horses do not like the whole flowers much and they will sort them out of a mix. In these cases it is best to grind them up in a food processor a little before mixing them with other feed.

Horehound (*Marrubrium vulgare*)

Parts used Leaves.

Actions Antiseptic, bitters, carminative, expectorant and tonic.

Contents Bitters, pinene, alkaloids, tannins and vitamin C.

Utility Useful for the treatment of colds, nasal and sinus congestion, coughs and chest infections. Horehound is also a gentle digestive and circulatory tonic.

Application Should be included as a hedgerow herb to allow self-medication for the above conditions. It is also useful in the respiratory tonics (described in the relevant sections) to improve respiratory efficiency and help clear mucous wastes from the nose, bronchioles and lungs.

Cautions None if supplied for self-medication.

Horseradish (*Cochlearia armoracia*)

Parts used Roots and leaves.

Actions Antibacterial, desensitizing, diaphoretic, diuretic, mucosal stimulant, rubefacient and vermifuge.

Contents Acetic acid, albumin, chlorine, enzymes, silica, sinigrin, starches and vitamin C, also contains useful amounts of phosphorous and sulfur.

Utility Horseradish is a useful tonic for the gall bladder and pancreas and a powerful tonic that promotes elimination through the bowel. However, for our purposes it is most useful in that it speeds the clearing of histamines from the blood, making it an important herb in the treatment of allergies while, at the same time, stimulating the mucosal linings of the upper respiratory system.

Application   Horseradish should be included in your hedgerow and in mixtures designed to treat sinus infection, inflammation or over-sensitivity – often all showing up together in cases of allergic rhinitis. It can also be useful in stimulating the bowel in cases where elimination is a little sluggish and dry.

Cautions   Not to be given in large amounts, or where there is any suspicion of ulcers in the stomach or gastrointestinal tract, as even small amounts could aggravate such problems.

Hypericum/St Johns Wort (*Hypericum perforatum*)

Parts used   Flowers and fresh top growth.

Actions   Nervine, topically antiseptic.

Contents   Calcium and zinc and other phosphates, along with hypericins, essential oils, flavonoids and resin.

Utility   For healing physically damaged nerves and for regulating an over-stimulated nervous system showing evidence through the skin as in eczema, heat rashes, low pain threshold, shingles and vitiligo.

Application   Hypericum is an important herb to support and speed the healing of damaged nerves when it can be given internally and applied externally in the oil form to the area. Hypericum can be given internally as a nervine tonic for the type of horse that shows superacuity of all five senses, is easily startled and often skin reactive, sweats excessively at times of stress and breaks out with skin irritations.

It also can be applied topically in the oil form or an extract wash for all reactive skin conditions and will also work with circulatory tonics like nettle to promote healthy coat and color.

Cautions   For internal use, start off initially with a small dose because, by definition, horses that need the herb are also supersensitive.

Juniper (*Juniperus communis*)

Parts used Berries.

Actions Carminative, diuretic, repellant and tonic.

Contents Contains potassium salts, lignin and is high in oily resins.

Utility Assists in clearing fluid retained in cell tissues and aids excretion through the kidneys and bladder (lignin is soothing to the kidneys). Juniper also has an unusual ability to soak up any adrenalin remaining in the system after stress or challenge. As a tea, it can be applied to wounds to discourage flies.

Application Juniper forms part of kidney breakdown and diuretic treatments paired with celery. Juniper tea is an excellent muscle relaxant and toner at the end of a competition day, when it will soak up excess adrenalin remaining in the horse's body, promote excretion of other wastes through the kidneys and restore the tone to heart function after serious effort.

Cautions Not to be given in any case of suspected kidney stones and not to be given in large amounts or too frequently as it will produce the opposite effect to that desired, i.e. it will weaken the kidneys, muscles and heart.

Kelp/bladderwrack (*Fucus vesiculosus*)

Parts used Whole herb.

Actions Alterative, demulcent and a metabolic regulator.

Contents Kelp is the highest plant source of iodine and bromine in compounds of sodium and potassium. It is mucilaginous and bitter and contains a complete range of trace elements and rare and common minerals in loosely bonded organic structures, which are easily absorbed into your horse's gut.

Utility As a natural regulator of thyroid and other hormones and as a complete source of trace elements.

Application As dried granules or powder or as an ingredient in feed blocks. It is best provided in a form in which the horse can choose his own dose requirements.

Cautions None if provided on demand or in small amounts daily (15–20 gm daily).

Linseed/Flax Seed (*Linum usitatissimum*)

Parts used Seeds.

Actions Emollient and demulcent.

Contents Minerals, mucilage 15%, fixed oil 30–40%, prussic acid.

Utility Specific utility is in supporting the healing and rejuvenation of ligaments. Linseed has the particular ability to re-tension stretched ligaments and relax overly tight or shortened ligaments.

Application As part of a treatment (along with millet, yarrow and comfrey) that will dramatically improve the rate and quality of healing of all tendon and bone injuries. Linseed also improves the color and shine of your horse's coat, is a valuable source of oil and helps to lubricate a dry bowel.

Cautions Medicinal quantities of the fresh, crushed raw seeds (do not buy ready-crushed seeds as the quality deteriorates rapidly) are half a cup twice daily. Preventative quantities are half that again. If feeding larger amounts than the above, the seeds should be crushed and then boiled or soaked, as the seeds contain traces of prussic acid, which is potentially toxic in large doses. *Do not feed linseed oil to your horse at all.*

Male Fern (*Dryopteris filix-mas*)

Parts used   Leaves.

Action   Vermicide, vermifuge and bitter tonic.

Contents   Filmaron, falicic acid, resin and tannins.

Utility   Specific tapeworm treatment: it kills and expels tapeworms. Generally applicable for other worms also.

Application   An extract is made from fresh or dried leaves: this can be vinegar-based or water-based. A large dose (about a quarter of a cup) is syringed down the horse's throat one evening and then again the following morning. The same dose is repeated after three weeks.

Cautions   There is no value in more frequent repetitions of the treatment but the whole program can be repeated after three months if you feel there is a threat from tapeworm.

Maritime Pine (*Pinus pinaster*)

Parts used   Bark, including sap.

Actions   Antioxidant, antiseptic, diuretic, diaphoretic and rubefacient.

Contents   Resin, from which is derived turpentine.

Utility   Pine water made from needles as a tea was traditionally given to horses with chronic cough and used internally, and externally as a cutaneous stimulant and antiseptic.

Application   The bark is used as either a tea or an extract, which provides a super antioxidant and circulatory tonic.

Cautions   Do not give tar or turpentine internally before talking to someone with experience.

Mullein (*Verbascum thapsus*)

Parts used Leaves and flowers.

Actions Antiseptic, astringent, demulcent, emollient and expectorant.

Contents Glucoside, gum, phosphates, resin and tannin.

Utility Used to relieve persistent coughs.

Application Utilized in preparations for respiratory complaints, specifically for the relief of symptoms to provide comfort to the horse while healing takes place.

Cautions None. The seeds are slightly narcotic and traditionally were used by poachers to intoxicate fish.

Nettle/Stinging Nettle (*Urtica dioica*)

Parts used Aerial parts (fresh or dried).

Actions Alterative, arterial tonic.

Contents Contains histamine, serotonin, chlorophyll, formic acid, as well as iron, potassium, silica, sodium and vitamins A and C.

Utility Powerful source of iron, an arterial tonic and blood oxygenator.

Application Nettle is a valuable source of organic iron compounds sometimes lacking in a horse's diet, particularly one living on 'improved pasture'. Iron tonics provided as supplements are not naturally occurring compounds (with the exception of molasses) and are poorly absorbed and utilized in the body. Use as a general tonic in the form of fresh green

plants from your hedgerow or the dried herb in feed when a handful of dried or fresh herb is appropriate (the fresh herb may be dunked in hot water to get rid of the sting if this is a problem). In cases of anemia, use the tea form with either dried or fresh herb, or a handful of stems mixed with feed.

Cautions For medical conditions such as anemia and bleeding from the lungs, nettle should be given in conjunction with the herb rue to support and balance venous circulation. Do not give nettle alone (without rue) to mares in foal but do allow them to pick for themselves as they wish from the hedgerow.

Oats (*Avena sativa*)

Parts used Whole plant, including seeds fresh and dried.

Actions Emollient and nervine.

Contents Contains alkaloids, flavonoids, protein, minerals – including silica and calcium – and vitamin E.

Utility Useful in cases of nervous exhaustion.

Application The fact that oats will make many horses too fizzy and unmanageable is an interesting case of too much of a good thing, which can produce the opposite to the desired effect. The correct amount of oats in a horse's feed will calm down a fizzy or hot temperament, while too much will produce the fizziness. Oats are a very valuable and natural feed for horses; give them routinely but first try out various doses to find the correct dose for each individual horse.

Cautions Dose sensitive, see above.

Parsley (*Petroselinum crispum*)

Parts used   Fresh or dried leaves and stems. Fresh parsley may be stored frozen.

Actions   Carminative, digestive, diuretic, emmenagogue and tonic.

Contents   Parsley is rich in vitamins A, B and C, contains significant amounts of calcium, copper, sodium, magnesium and iron, along with chlorophyll, enzymes and fatty acids.

Utility   A very powerful iron and central-nervous-system tonic. Also a powerful stimulant to the kidneys, which means it should be used with care because kidney stones can be dislodged under its influence. Mineral source generally and iron source in particular.

Application   Make parsley available in the hedgerow; give a quarter of a cup of dried leaves or a small bunch of fresh parsley at irregular intervals as a supplement. For medical complaints make a tea from similar quantities and dose twice daily. It is a useful tonic for the breeding mare and an excellent vegetable tonic for dogs.

Cautions   Use small amounts only. Do not give it if there is any chance of kidney stones. Never feed to birds or pet rabbits, it does not suit their digestive system and has been fatal to birds.

Passion Flower (*Passiflora incarnata*)

Parts used   Leaves.

Actions   Antispasmodic, hypotensive, nervine and sedative.

Contents   Alkaloids, flavonoids and sterols.

Utility   Especially useful in breaking into habitual nervous-system patterns.

Application   Combined with other nervines when seeking to reverse the habitual component of nervous-system difficulties. A suitable dose for your horse would be two tablespoons of dried herb a day, either mixed with feed or made into a tea and split between two feeds.

Cautions   None.

Pennyroyal (*Mentha pulegiuim*)

Parts Used   Leaves.

Action   Carminative, diaphoretic, emmenagogue, stimulant and vermicide.

Contents   Volatile oil.

Utility   Mosquito and flea repellent. Useful to help promote estrus when it is abnormally absent, e.g. for the racing mare after hormone treatments.

Application   For use as an insect repellent, pennyroyal can be extracted or made into a tea and sprayed on a damp coat. Alternatively, dab the tea around the eyes or other sensitive areas. Pennyroyal's other main use is to help bring on estrus in a mare when she has not come in to season when expected.

Cautions   None for external use. Consult an herbalist experienced in its use for internal applications.

Peppermint (*Mentha piperita*)

Parts used   Aerial parts.

Actions   Anti-emetic, carminative, diaphoretic and antiseptic.

Contents   Volatile oils, including menthol and pinene, flavonoids and rosmarinic acid.

Utility   A digestive tonic and aid to cooling through perspiration.

Application   Used as a preventative and aid for colic attacks or tendencies, helpful for a sluggish digestive system generally and, along with other herbs like fenugreek, is used for treating 'the puffs'. Grow alongside your water troughs.

Cautions   None.

Raspberry Leaf (*Rubus idaeus*)

Parts used   Leaves fresh or dried.

Actions   Astringent and emmenagogue.

Contents   Contains flavonoids, polypeptides and tannins and is high in folic acid.

Utility   To prompt fertility and to relax and tone up the uterus for ease of carrying, foaling and recovery after delivery.

Application   Breeding mares should be on raspberry leaf in dried plant or tea form for the whole of the breeding cycle up until weaning. Add half a cup of dried herb to your mare's feed daily.

Cautions   None at the prescribed doses.

Red Clover (*Trifolium pratense*)

Parts used   Flowers fresh or dried.

Actions   Alterative.

Contents   High in iron and contains both copper and cobalt, along with isoflavons, flavonoids and coumarins.

Utility   Red clover improves the size, health and number of red blood cells and platelets. It also has a specific utility in that it breaks down the walls of cysts, wherever they are found in the body, allowing the cysts to discharge into the blood stream.

Application   The action of red clover has the effect of raising hemoglobin levels, making it powerful treatment for blood disorders. It is consequently used as a component in treatments for anemia and other blood disorders, as well as for blood poisoning.

Cautions   Apart from being selected by the horse as fresh green pasture on demand, red clover should be given in small

amounts, under supervision and partnered with several other herbs because it can produce a major blood imbalance and/or a very powerful toxic shock. It should be partnered with echinacea to support a normal balance between white and red blood cells, and with garlic to assist in toxin processing if they are released into the blood stream. Hypericum should also be considered in a mix as this is high in zinc and can further ameliorate adverse reactions.

Rosehips/Briar Rose (*Rosa canina*)

Parts used   The hips (these are the small olive-shaped red resinous seed pods left over after flowering, which are best left to dry on the bush).

Actions   Alterative, diuretic, hepatic, nervine and tonic.

Contents   One of the very best sources of biotin, iron and vitamin C with traces of copper making it one of nature's most mutually supportive combinations.

Utility   Rosehips appear dozens of times during this treatise as an iron and vitamin C source and for the blood, the liver, the kidneys, the adrenal glands, the circulation and the immune system.

Application   Make rosehips tea for your horses daily as a preventative and you will not need to use it in medical situations.

Cautions   None.

Rosemary (*Rosmarinus officinalis*)

Parts used   Leaves.

Actions   Antiseptic, anti-inflammatory, antispasmodic, cerebro-circulatory stimulant, nervine and vasodilator.

Contents   Volatile oils, flavonoids, rosmarinic acid, tannins and resin.

Utility   Internally for coat and skin health and for improving blood supply to the muscles and the brain. Externally as an oil or a wash made from a tea for reducing muscular cramps, tension and soreness after exercise.

Application For show horses, as part of their regular feed, for the benefits to coat and skin health. An important additive in a mixture for an equine athlete in very heavy work (such as endurance, eventing, racing or pacing), when the horse is required to concentrate and work muscles very hard. The effect of rosemary in these cases is to supply the brain with extra oxygen, helping the horse to keep his focus. Rosemary also enhances circulation to the muscles so that they are better nourished and acid waste products are more readily cleared away. This results in less vascular damage, allowing the horse to work more smoothly and recover more quickly from such work. The suggested dose is two tablespoons a day mixed with feed.

Cautions Do not feed to pregnant mares because rosemary can cause a sudden stimulatory effect to aspects of the circulatory system; it is preferable not to expose a fetus to such stimulation.

Rue (*Ruta graveolens*)

Parts used Leaves and stems.

Actions Alterative, antianemic, vulnerary.

Contents Bitters, rutin (vitamin P), tannin and vitamin K.

Utility Strengthens blood-vessel and capillary walls, especially in the lungs and the venous system. Rue also helps with eyesight afflictions, is included in anemia mixes and counteracts some rat poisons. In this case it should be given with apricot kernel oil, which is a very high natural source of vitamin K.

Application Important in the treatment of bleeders as it strengthens capillary walls and increases capillary action and blood supply. With vitamin K, rue also helps to break up the venous congestion that so often results from blood pressure changes; these are the two components in the bleeding condition affecting pacers and racers especially. As an eye treatment, washing the eyes with rue tea will reduce inflammation and soreness. A quarter of a cup twice a day is a sufficient medical dose. Supplementary doses should be a half or a third of this.

Cautions Rue should always be given in conjunction with nettle to maintain the balance between the arterial and venous systems. Never give in large amounts to pregnant mares because this herb can cause a sudden stimulatory effect to aspects of the circulatory system (similar to the actions of rosemary), which can have harmful effects on the fetus. People with sensitive skin should be careful when handling rue because reactions can occur.

Sage (*Salvia officinalis*)

Parts used Leaves.

Actions Alterative, astringent, cerebro-circulatory tonic and pituitary tonic.

Contents Volatile oils including thujone and camphor, flavonoids, rosmarinic acid, estrogenic substances and tannins.

Utility A cerebro-circulatory tonic, which strengthens the heart, improves brain and memory function and heightens the senses. Also reputedly used for treatment of rheumatic complaints.

Application Useful in small amounts in mixes assisting to condition young horses. Useful medically when there are signs of slower than normal development, when it will act as a 'catch-up tonic' along with comfrey and nettle.

Cautions Do not feed to pregnant mares because this herb can cause a sudden stimulatory effect to aspects of the circulatory system (similar to that caused by rosemary and rue). Best left in the hedgerow for your horses to choose for themselves. Make a cup of sage tea for yourself to improve your own memory!

Slippery Elm (*Ulmus fulva*)

Parts used   Powdered inner bark.

Actions   Carminative, demulcent, emollient and mucilaginous.

Contents   Contains calcium and phosphates in a natural balance with large amounts of mucilage and some tannin.

Utility   Slippery elm soothes inflammation internally right through the digestive tract and allows a damaged or irritated mucosal lining to heal.

Application   Valuable for scouring and for treating colic when mixed with cold chamomile tea. This mixture will allow ulceration and colitis to heal and

settle. It can be used as an effective poultice medium to draw out and clean wounds – with castor oil, for example. Internal dose is one third of a cupful mixed with chamomile tea to make a slurry, which is then added to a bran mash or mixed with other feed. This dose to be given twice daily.

Cautions   None. Can be mixed with mother's milk and given to day-old foals. Watch for poor quality supply however; quality slippery elm has a sweetish aromatic smell and is a finely ground light-brown powder with no bitter taste. Check it before you buy.

Tansy (*Tanacetum vulgare*)

Parts used   Leaves and tops.

Actions   Insect repellent.

Contents   Tanacetin, tannic acid, volatile oil and resins.

Utility   Bruised leaves will release insect-repelling oils, which can be rubbed directly onto the horse's coat. Extracts from the fresh herb can be made and stored for use in external sprays for the same purpose.

Application   Insect repellent.

Cautions   Do not use internally.

Thuja (*Thuja occidentalis*)

Parts used   Young leafy twigs.

Actions   Alterative, antiparasitic and antifungal.

Contents   Bitters, camphor, tannic acid, volatile oils and thujin.

Utility   Thuja is the tallest of the cedar trees and is an unusual and rather unpredictable herb, which is proving more and more valuable in treating exotic infections.

Application   Useful in the concentrated form for wart treatments; dab directly on the wart once a day. Useful also as an external insect and parasite repellent, and as an antifungal treatment. In this case a spray can be made up with extracts of other antiparasitic herbs in vinegar and a small amount, say twenty drops per liter, of thuja extract added (obtain the commercial 1:1 extract from your herbal pharmacy). This is then sprayed onto a damp coat and allowed to dry. Thuja in combination with colloidal silver – both internally and externally – is proving to be a successful treatment for Golden Staph, a hospital-based 'superbug' infection, which will shortly show up in veterinary hospitals, if it is not already there.

Cautions   Leave internal use to the professional herbalist.

Thyme (*Thymus vulgaris*)

Parts used   Leaves, dried or fresh.

Actions   Antiseptic, antiviral, carminative, fumigant and insecticide.

Contents   Volatile oils including thymol and pinene, flavonoids and tannins.

Utility   Burned as an insecticide and fumigant and is an excellent antiseptic and antiviral – especially for throat infections.

Application   Burn dried leaves in the stable complex and include a tea or extract in mixtures along with garlic, lemon and rosehips for throat and respiratory infections. Grow in the hedgerow.

Cautions   None when given in small doses.

Valerian (*Valeriana officinalis*)

Parts used   Dried roots.

Action   Antispasmodic, hypotensive, nervine and sedative.

Contents   Contains valerinic acid and other volatile oils, indoids, alkaloids, flavonoids and tannins. It is high in organic compounds of silica, magnesium and phosphorous.

Utility   Promotes sleep by relaxing muscular tension and spasm. Relaxes the physically uptight nervous system that shows up in bit-grinding and jerky movement in competition. Add to dried feed, finely crushed, at a rate of one tablespoon a day. Probably best given as vinegar-based extract, since the herb is not all that palatable to many horses and they will cleverly sort it out of a mix. Valerian has a very distinctive smell and your horse may decide on first contact that he does not want to have anything to do with it.

Application   As a nervine in a mixture for a horse of the valerian type (see Chapter 4: Nerve Tonics).

Cautions   Can have a laxative effect on horses in larger doses.

Vervain (*Verbena officinalis*)

Parts used   Leaves and flowering heads.

Actions   Antispasmodic, hepatic, nervine, tonic and sedative.

Contents   Minerals, including phosphates, but the ingredients are not studied fully as yet.

Utility   Specific for those horses that appear permanently agitated, distracted and fidgety. They often also have overly sensitive skin.

Application   As a component in a nervous-system mix to suit the particular vervain-type nervous system, (see Chapter 4: Nerve Tonics). A daily dose of two tablespoons of dried herb is sufficient mixed with other feed.

Cautions   None at the recommended dose levels. Remember more is not better and if vervain does not calm your horse, you will have to rethink your own assessment of his requirements. Do not just simply try more and more of the herb.

White Willow (*Salix alba*)

Parts used   Bark.

Actions   Analgesic, anti-inflammatory, antiseptic, astringent, febrifuge and tonic.

Contents   Contains phenolic glycosides (including salicin), esters (including salicylic acid), tannins and flavonoids. This is the herb from which the modern aspirin was derived.

Utility   Relieves pain, inflammation and fever.

Application   Used to treat rheumatic and arthritic pain and as a component in all treatments for pain and inflammation resulting from stress or injury. It is either extracted from the powdered bark, along with other herbs, in a vinegar-based mix, or added in commercial extract form to oil treatments like the hoof oil (see Chapter 10: Founder).

Cautions   None if used in prescribed amounts.

Wintergreen (*Gaultheria procumbens*)

Parts used   Leaves.

Actions   Anti-inflammatory, antirheumatic and rubefacient.

Contents   Phenolic compounds including salicylic acid, gaultherin, vanillic and caffeic acids, volatile oils and methyl salicylate.

Utility   Deeply penetrating heating and vulnerary action combining anti-inflammatory action, making it ideal to penetrate deep muscle areas or dense tissues.

Application   As an ingredient in healing oils and creams and irreplaceable in oils designed for healing within the hoof (see Chapter 10: Founder).

Cautions   Can cause blistering if massaged in too vigorously and can cause swelling and distress in anything but tiny amounts when used in external treatments for the lower limbs (excepting the hoof). Amounts of 5% of a cream or oil is sufficient for big muscles and hooves and less than 1% in areas poorly served by circulation like the lower limbs.

Wormwood (*Artemisia absinthium*)

Parts used   Leaves and flowering tops.

Actions   Anti-inflammatory and vermifuge.

Contents   Contains camphorated volatile oils, lactones, flavonoids, phenolic acid and lignans.

Utility   To manage worms and other internal parasites.

Application   Grow wormwood bushes close to the water trough and allow your horses to self-medicate. Make up a wormwood extract in molasses for regular dosing according to a program (see Chapter 4: Worming).

Cautions   Safe in recommended doses.

Yarrow/Woundwort
(*Achillea millefolium*)

Parts used   Stems, leaves and flowers.

Actions   Alterative, anti-inflammatory, antipyretic, astringent, diaphoretic and tonic.

Contents   Flavonoids (including apigenin and rutin), iron, tannins and volatile oils.

Utility   A powerful styptic and astringent, yarrow will reverse fluid accumulation and staunch hemorrhage. It has a deflammatory action on swollen tissues, enabling wounds to close naturally from the inside out and to heal with the minimum of scarring (see antiseptic/styptic treatment in Chapter 4: Herbal First Aid). Yarrow also supports bone-marrow production of red blood cells and acts as an iron tonic in cases of severe debility.

Application   Used as a component in blood-quality, bleeder and recovery mixes and in immune-system mixes for the boost given to iron levels and the central nervous system. Usually used in support of anti-infective and antioxidant herbs.

Cautions   None.

References

Robert McDowell's mail order and free consultation services, email addresses and web pages are to be found through:

www.herbal-treatments.com.au

For further exploration of natural horsekeeping, the relationship between man and horse, and further herbal and related alternative studies, the following publications may be of interest:

Boericke, William. *Materia Medica with Repertory & 50 Homeopathic Drugs*, B. Jain Publishers Ltd., New Delhi.

Chancellor, Philip M. *Handbook of the Bach Flower Remedies*, Keats Publishing Inc., Connecticut, 1971.

De Bairacli Levy, Juliette. *The Complete Herbal Handbook for Farm and Stable*, Faber and Faber, London, 1991.

Dorrance, Tom. *True Unity*, Give-It-A-Go Enterprises, Tuscarora, Nevada, 1990.

Grieve, Mrs. M. *A Modern Herbal* (Revised Edition), Tiger Books International, London, 1973.

Hall, Dorothy. *Dorothy Hall's Herbal Medicine*, Thomas C. Lothian Pty Ltd, Melbourne, 1988.

Hunt, Ray. *Think Harmony With Horses*, Pioneer Publishing, California, 1991.

Jackson, Jaime. *The Natural Horse*, Star Ridge, California, 1997.

MacLeod, G. *The Treatment of Horses by Homeopathy*, C.W. Daniel Co. Ltd., England, 1988.

Index

Note: Page numbers in **bold** type refer to major discussions of a topic or herb

abrasions 167–8
abscess, foot 178–81
Achillea millefolium see yarrow
aconitum 144
acupuncture 187
adrenaline 124
aggression 229–30
agrimony 137
alcohol-based extracts 35–6
aldosterone 238
alfalfa (lucerne) 62, **246–7**
allantoin 194
allergic reactions 73–5, **154–5**
allergic rhinitis 190–2
    herbal mix recipe 221–2
Allium sativum see garlic
aloe vera 93, 205, 243, **247**
alternative therapies 142, 150–1
    homeopathy 48–9, **142–6**, 155, 170
    need for knowledge 17–18
    revolution in 15–17, 151
    see also Bach Flower Remedies
alternatives 235–6
anemia 155–7
    causes 155–6
    herbal mixes 156–7, 220
    prevention 156
anhydrosis 205–6
anodynes 236–7
Anthemis nobilis see chamomile

anti-inflammatories 76–9
    conventional drugs 76–8
    herbal 78–9
antibiotics 74, **79–83**, 235–6
    colloidal silver **81–3**, 173, 201
    discovery 79–80
    drug resistance 80–1
    foot infections 179
antihistamines 154
antioxidants 83–4
antipruritics 237
antiseptic/styptic mixes 92, 97, 218
antiseptics 237–8
antispasmodics 238
apis mellifica 144, 155
Apium graveolens see celery
arnica 78, 91, 97, 144, 186, 225, 245, **248**
    ointment 94, 111, 162, 165, 166, 167, 187
arsenicum 145
Artemisia absinthium see wormwood
arterial bleeding 96
arthritis 76–8, 109
    causes 160–1
    herbal mixes 162–3
    prevention 161–2
aspen 140, 147
aspirin 62, 76–7
astringents 238
Australia
    Hendra virus 197–8
    racehorse wastage 125
Avena sativa see oats
azoturia 158–60

Bach Flower Remedies **146–50**
    allergic rhinitis 191
    common treatments 148–50
    endurance horse 116
    horse/rider combination 140
    inflammation 78
    respiratory infections 189
    stringhalt 208
    traveling 137–8
Bach Flower Rescue Remedy 78, 100, 101,
    126, **147**
      for allergic reactions 154
      azoturia 159
      broodmare 126
      colic 170
      eye problems 176
      first aid 91–2, 97
      laminitis 186
bacteria, antibiotic resistance 80–1
bananas 241
bandages 112
Bathurst Traditional Medicine Center 224, 225
bee stings 205
behavioral problems
    case studies 228–9, 230–1
    stallion 123
belladonna 145
bicarbonate of soda 205
bioflavonoids 88
biting insects 204–5
bitters 239
blackcurrants 157
bladderwrack *see* kelp
'bleeders' 192–4
bleeding 96–7
blending herbs 46
    'buckshot' approach 47–8
'blisters' 244
blood cleansers 73–5, 109–10, **235–6**
body builders 84
body condition 184
bog bean 163
bone and tendon mix 218–19, 225
boots, protective 111–12
borage 105, 116, 124, 214, 215, **248**
Bracket Jack 226–7
bran 46–7, 63–4
breeding 122–3
    broodmare management 125–7
    stallion management 123–5
    young horse management 127–9
brittle feet 181–2
broodmare 107, 125–7
broom 28, 36
bryonia 145
Buck 223–5
'buckshot' approach 47–8
buckwheat 157, **249**
burdock 76, 78
'bute' *see* phenylbutazone

caffeine 120
cajeput oil 86, 87, 244
calcium 89
calendula 92, 97, 218, **249**
canine herbal practice 36
car tires, as plant pots 55–6
Carmelita 230–1
carminatives 239
case studies
    Bracket Jack 226–7

    Buck 223–6
    Carmelita 230–1
    Harry 231–2
    Jackson 228–9
    Kachét 225
    Pepper 227–8
    Shalimar 229–30
castor oil 176, 180, 240, **250**
    poultices 86
cathartics 240
celandine 176, 177
celery 163, 241, **250**
cerrato 147–8
chamomile 137, 155, 174, 215, **251**
    tea 95, **217**
    topical use 202, 205
chamomile-type horse 67–8, 108
cherry plum 148
chest and immunity tonic 188–9, **220–1**
chickweed 202, **252**
chilli 244
choline 89, 239
cider vinegar extracts **36–9**, 162
citronella oil 206
clematis 148
Clostridium tetani 209
clover, red, *see* red clover
coat
    color 49
    condition 214–16
    show-coat mix 215, 219
Cochlearia armoracia see horseradish
cod-liver oil 215
colic 168–71
    case studies 223–6, 228–9
    causes 168–9
    first aid 169–70
    herbal mixes 170–1
    prevention 170
collection of herbs 26–30
colloidal silver **81–3**, 173, 201
coltsfoot 189
comfrey 78–9, 98, 112, 154, 157, 207, **252**
    extract 100, 162, 186
    fresh leaf 167, 194, 208
    poultices 165, 166, 167
competition, and herbs 120
conjunctivitis 175–7
cool-down strategy 112
cornea, ulcerated 176
crab apple 148–9
Crataegus oxycanthus see hawthorn
cuts *see* wounds
cysts 172

dandelion 105, 137, 198, 202–3, 214, 215, 239,
    243, **253**
      root 29, 163, 174, 242
debility
    mild stress-induced 213–14
    severe 212–13
    terminally severe 210–12, 260–1
demulcents 194, 240
dermatophilosis 203–4
desensitizing injections 74
devil's claw 76, 78, 79, **254**
diaphorectics 241
diarrhea 173–5, 219
diet
    basic 63–5
    broodmare 126

oats 64–5, 68–9
digestive system
    chamomile horse 67–8
    disorders 168–75
diuretics 240–1
domestication of horse 13–14, 21–2
dose levels **39–42**, 174–5
    dry herbs 42
    homeopathic 41
    'more is better' approach 48–9
    physical 40–1
    trigger 41–2
drenches, colic 170
dressage horse 140
    case study 225
drug resistance 80–1
drug testing 120
drugs 198
    'magic bullet' approach 62
    side effects 77
    toxicity 78, 231–2
drying of herbs 27–30
Dryopteris filix-mas see male fern

echinacea 172–3, 173, 180, 181, 203, 207, **254**
elecampane 188, 194, **255–6**
electrolytes 71–3, 205–6
elm *see* slippery elm
emmenogogues 242
emollients 240
endurance horse
    case study 223–6
    performance enhancement 115–16
ephedrine 120
equine herpesvirus 196–7
equine influenza 195–6
equine morbillivirus 198
equisetum (horsetail) 78–9, 112, 186, 206, 207,
    255
eucalyptus 94, 196, 201, **256**
euphorbia 154
exercise-induced pulmonary hemorrhage
(EIPH) 192–4
exotic infections 197–8
extracts
    alcohol-based 35–6
    honey/molasses/oil 33–5
    method of making 38–9
    vinegar-based 36–9, 46
eye conditions 175–8
eyewash 93

Fagopyrum esculentum see buckwheat
farrier 185
febrifuges 242
feeding 63–4
    basic diet 64–5
    broodmare 126
    herbal mixes 42, 46–7
    herbal teas 44
    oats 64–5, 68–9
fennel 95, 174, **257**
fenugreek 173, 188–9, 196, 203, 206, 215, 240,
    257–8
fever 242
fibrotic ossifying myopathy 225
first aid
    colic 169–70
    kit 92–5
    shock 91–2
    wounds 92, 96–9

flax seed *see* linseed
Fleming, Alexander 80
fluid balance 205–6
fluid removal 238
fly bites 204–5
foal 107, 127–8
Foeniculum vulgare see fennel
founder *see* laminitis
free radicals 83
fresh herbs 31
Fucus vesiculosus see kelp
fungal infections, skin 200–2

gardens, herb 32, 51, 54–6
garlic 180, 189, **258**
    antibiotic/antiseptic actions 81, 195–6
    molasses extract 34–5, 45
    poultice 86
    tonic 90
    for worming 75–6
Gaultheria procumbens see wintergreen
gentian 239
ginger 170
golden seal 176, 177, **259**
'Golden Staph' 81, 201–2
grazing 13, 14, 21
greasy heel 87, **203–4**
groundsel 87
growing herbs 51–2
    choosing plants 56–8
    in gardens 51, 54–6
    in hedgerows 52–4
guaiacum 76, 78, 79

hair growth 87, 202
Hall, Dorothy 146, 176
Harpogophytum procumbens see devil's
    claw
Harry 231–2
harvesting herbs 26–30
hawthorn 97, 100, 106, 116, 194, **259–61**
    berry extract 137
    hedges 52–3
hay fever *see* allergic rhinitis
health, perfect 102–3
hedgerows, herbal 52–4
Hendra virus 197–8
hepar sulph 145
hepatics (liver tonics) 23–4, 137, 202–3, **242–3**
herbal teas 69, 95
    feeding 44
    making 43–5
herbs
    actions of 22–4
    choosing/buying 56–8
    collection and drying 26–30
    growing in gardens 51, 54–6
    growing in hedges 52–4
    reactions to 49–50
    safety 39–40, 50
    sources of 24–5
    storage 31–9
    use of fresh 31
    value of 21–2
herpesvirus, equine 196–7
histamines 155
holistic treatment 61–3
homeopathic dose 41
homeopathy 48–9, **142–6**
    allergy treatment 155
    colic treatment 170

common treatments 144–6
dilutions 143–4
honey 170
    herbal extracts 33–5
honeysuckle 78, 149
hoof-oil mix 94, 100–1, 186, 204
    recipe 219–20
hooves 178–87
    abscesses 178–81
    brittle 181–2
    bruises 187
    sand crack 87
    see also laminitis
hops 68, 105, 137, 214, **261**
hops-type horse 68
horehound 196, **262**
horse-rider team 139–41
horsebox design 132–3
horseradish 154, 155, **262–3**
horsetail see equisetum
hospital infections 81
humans
    herbal practice 36, 68
    sharing herbs with horses 139–41
Humulus lupulus see hops
Hydrastis canadensis see golden seal
hydrogen peroxide 97
hypericum (St John's wort) 28, 34, 69, 87, 145,
    202, **263**

immune system 73–5, 100
    antioxidants for 83–4
    chest and immunity mixture 188–9, **220–1**
    respiratory infections 187–8
    support herbs 203
impatiens 149
inflammation 77–8
influenza, equine 195–6
injections 99–101
    precautions 101
    vein damage 100–1
injuries
    prevention 117–18
    rest and recuperation 118–20
insect bites 204–5
internal ulcer mix 219
Inula helenium see elecampane
iron 89, 156, 156–7, 202
itch 204–5
itching 237

Jackson 228–9
juniper 241, **264**
junk food 64

Kachét 225
kali bich 145
kelp 105, 127, 162, 186, 189, 194, 215, **264–5**
    electrolytes 71–2
    poultice mix 87
    tonic 90
knowledge
    need for 17–18
    traditional 14–15, 26–7

laminitis 183–7
    acute 184
    case study 227–8, 231–2
    causes 182–5
    herbal remedies 86, 186–7
    prevention 185–6

larch 149
lavender oil 94, 205
laxatives 43
legal use of herbs 120
lemon 101, 189, 199, 201
lifestyle, of horse 13–14, 21–2
ligament problems 163–5
linseed 90, 162, 167, **265**
    for ligaments and tendons 164
    oil 98, 165, 166, 186
    poultice 85–6, 87
    toxicity 164
Linum usitatissimum see linseed
liquorice 203
liver tonics (hepatics) 23–4, 137, 202–3, **242–3**
lucerne (alfalfa) 62, **246–7**
lungs 192–4
lymphatic system 206

'magic bullet' approach 62
magnesium phosphate 66, 208
male fern **266**
mare see broodmare
marigold see calendula
maritime pine 16, 36, 84, 106, 111, 112, **116**,
    137, 189, 203, 208, **266**
Marrubium vulgare see horehound
marshmallow 189, 194
massage 151, 238
mastitis 86
measurements 10
Medicago sativa see alfalfa (lucerne)
medicine
    orthodox 16, 62, 74, 198, 235–6
    traditional 14–15
Mentha piperita see peppermint
Mentha pulegium see pennyroyal
millet 90, 100, 162, 164, 166, 167
mimulus 149
mineral supplements 88
mint 206
mistletoe 207
molasses 243
    herb extracts 33–5, 45
monasteries 32
Moon Blindness 177–8
'more is better' approach 48–9
mugwort 208
mullein 189, **267**
Multi Drug Resistant bacteria 80–1
mustard oil 86, 244

navicular disease 165–6
neoprene-type boots 111
nervines **65–70**, 114, **243–4**
    feeding 69–70
nervous disorders 65–6
nervous system
    balance 70
    racing/pacing horses 107–8
    tonics **65–70**, 114, **243–4**
    types of 65–8, 107–8
nettle 100, 105, 156–7, 189, 194, 198, 202, 214,
    215, 244, **267–8**
nux vomica 49, 145

oats 64–5, **68–9**, 164, **268**
O'Hanlon, Tom 11–12
oil extracts 33–5
older horse 163
olive oil 33, 34

pacers
    bleeding 192–4
    herbal support 108–10
    nerves 107–8
pain
    natural role of 77–8
    relief of 76–8, 97, 98, **236–7**
parasites
    intestinal 75–6, 215, 245
    skin 200–2
parsley 124, 126–7, **269**
Passiflora incarnata see passion flower
passion flower 69, 114, **269**
'past-life' readings 151
pasture
    care 75
    hedges 52–4
pawpaw 87, 240
pencillin 80
pennyroyal 242, **270**
Pepper 227–8
peppermint **270**
perfect health 102–3
performance horse
    electrolytes 72–3
    injury prevention 117–18
    perfect health 102–3
    performance enhancement 103–6, 114–15
    prepurchase examination 120
    rest and recuperation 118–20, 213–14
    tendon damage 110–11
    tendon management 111–13
    trauma treatment 95–9
    see also racehorse
peritonitis 171–3
Petroselinum crispum see parsley
phenylbutazone (bute) **77–8**, 79, 160
    toxicity 78, 231–2
physical dose 40–1
phyto-hormones 125
pine bark *see* maritime pine
Pinus pinaster see maritime pine
pneumonia 81
poplar buds 87
potassium 241
poultices 84–7
    drawing mix 218
    for foot abscess 179–80
    herbal mixes 85–7
    for navicular disease 166
    reasons for use 85
    sensitivity testing 87
    for splints 167
    tendon/ligament/scar-tissue mix 218
prohibited substances 120
proud flesh 87
prunes 243
psyllium husk 170
'puffs', the 205–6
pulsatilla 145
puncture wounds 86
purchase examination 120–1
pus, in foot 178–81
pycnogenol 83–4

racehorse
    bleeding 192–4
    breeding *see* breeding
    herbal support 108–10
    nervous types and management 107–8
    recycling/retraining 113–15

stress-induced debility 213–14
    tendon management 110–13, 163–5
    wastage 125
    young horse management 117, 127–9
rain scald 203–4
raspberry leaf 126–7, **271**
reactions, to herbs 49–50
recovery
    mild debility 213–14
    performance horse 118–20
    severe debilitation 212–13
recurrent uveitis 177–8
red clover 125, 173, 180–1, 203, **271**
respiratory infections 187–90
    causes 187–8
    herbal mixes 188–90
respiratory system 187–99
rest 118–20
rheumatism 76–8, 109, 160–3
rhinitis, allergic *see* allergic rhinitis
rhus tox 146
Ricinus communis see castor oil
roaring 199
rock salt 71
rock water 149
Rosa canina see rosehips
rosehips 78, 97, 105–6, 116, 124, 136, 157, **272**
    tea 95, 163, 189, 196, **217**
rosemary 105, 111, 162, 214, 215, **272–3**
    oil 86, 87, 186, 238
Rosmarinus officinalis see rosemary
rubefacients 244–5
Rubus idaeus see raspberry leaf
rue 100, 157, 176, 177, 194, 245, **273–4**
Ruta graveolens see rue
rutin 157

safety, of herbs 39–40, 50
sage 208, **274**
St John's wort 28, 34, 69, 87, 145, 202, **263**
St Mary's thistle 203, 243
Salix alba see white willow
salts 70, 71–3, 205–6
Salvia officinalis see sage
sand colic 170
sand cracks 87
sarcoids 206–7
saw palmetto 208
scours 173–5, 219
seaweed *see* kelp
sedatives 65
seeds, harvesting 29–30
self-medication 72
senna 243
Shalimar 229–30
shampoos 215
shin soreness 167
shock 91–2, 126
show-coat mix 215, 219
showjumper, case study 226–7
silica 89, 90, 164, 181, 241
silver, colloidal **81–3**, 173, 201
skin conditions 73–4, 200–7
slippery elm 86, 174, 199, 240, **275**
snack foods 64
soy 125
spleen 154
splints 166–7
stallion management 123–5
Staphylococcus aureus, multidrug resistant
    81, 201–2

Stellaria media see chickweed
steroid treatments 74
stinging nettle *see* nettle
stone bruises 187
storage of herbs 31–9
stress, recovery 213–14
stringhalt 208
strychnine poisoning 49
styptics 92, 97, 218
supplements 21, 88, 156
    broodmare 126–7
sweating 241
    inability (anhydrosis) 205–6
swollen legs 87
Symphytum officinale see comfrey

Tanacetum vulgare see tansy
tannins 238–9, 245
tansy **275**
Taraxacum officinale see dandelion
teas *see* herbal teas
tendon and bone mix 218–19, 225
tendons
    bowed 163–5
    damage in performance horse 110–11
    management 111–13
terminally-severe debility 210–12, 260–1
tetanus 209
thuja (*Thuja occidentalis*) 87, 101, 172, 173, 201, 204, 207, **276**
thyme (*Thymus vulgaris*) 189, 201, **276–7**
tires, as plant pots 55–6
tonics
    general health 89–90
    nerve 65–70
    for performance horse 104–6
toxins, release of 73–5
trace elements 89
traditional healers 14–15
trailer
    design 132–3
    loading horse 131–2
tranquillizers 65
trauma
    herbal treatment 95–9
    pain and inflammation 77–8
    shock 91–2
    traveling 135
traveling 95, 130–1
    commercial vehicle 134–5
    dangers 131
    herbs for 135–8
    private vehicle 133–4
    trailer/truck design 132–3
    training for 131–2
Trifolium pratense see red clover
trigger dose 41–2
Trigonella foenum-graecum see fenugreek
truck design 132–3
'tying-up' (azoturia) 158–60
typhoid 81

Ulmus fulva see slippery elm
Urtica dioica see nettle

uveitis, recurrent 177–8

vaccinations **99–101**
    equine influenza 195
    tetanus 209
valerian 67, 208, **277**
Valeriana officinalis see valerian
valerian-type horse 66–7, 108
vein damage 100–1
Verbascum thapsus see mullein
Verbena officinalis see vervain
vermicides 245
vermifuges 245
vervain 23, 67, 136, 207, **278**
vervain-type horse 67, 108
veterinary examination 120–1
veterinary science 152
veterinary surgeon
    colic treatment 169–71
    and herbal medicine 152
    trauma treatment 96, 97, 98, 99
vices, stable 67
vine 78, 140, 150
vinegar 201
vinegar-based extracts **36–9**, 162
    doses 46
    making 38–9
violet leaves 203, 207
vitamin A 88, 143
vitamin B 88
vitamin C 83, 84, 88–9
vitamin D 89
vitamin E 83, 84, 89
vulnaries 245

walnut 78, 149–50
warm-up strategy 111–12
warts 207
water trough 53
watercress 239
weightlifters 84
wet-the-bed *see* dandelion
wheat germ 90
white chestnut 150
white willow 62, **76–7**, 162, 164, 186, **278**
winter coat 215–16
wintergreen 86, 111, 162, 165, 186, **279**
witch hazel cream 100
worming 75–6, 215, 245
wormwood 75–6, 215, 245, **279**
wounds 167–8
    first aid 92, 96–9
    orthodox treatment 96
    poultices 86
    tetanus 209

X-rays 120–1

yarrow 78, 92, 100, 104, **116**, 157, 162, 165, 189, 194, 199, 218, **280**
yearling sales 129
yogurt 208
young horse 115, 127–9
    starting/training 117, 128